# THE ULTIMATE
# COLORADO AVALANCHE
# TRIVIA BOOK

A Collection of Amazing Trivia Quizzes
and Fun Facts for Die-Hard Avalanche Fans!

**Ray Walker**

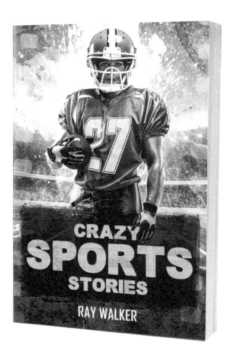

# CONTENTS

# INTRODUCTION

The roots of the Colorado Avalanche can be traced back to Quebec City in 1972. The franchise started out as the Quebec Nordiques in the World Hockey Association (WHA) and eventually made it to the NHL.

The Nordiques were one of four WHA franchises accepted by the NHL in 1979, when the two leagues partially merged. Of course, the team's loyal fan base followed their favorite club no matter what league they played in and would prove just how passionate they were 16 years later.

When 1995 arrived, the Nordiques were in financial dire straits. Instead of folding, they packed up and moved when a Denver, Colorado, business saved the day by buying the franchise.

This means that their fans have followed them from east to west and from Canada to America as the club was re-named the Colorado Avalanche. The next chapter began in 1995-96, when they defied the odds by winning the Stanley Cup in their very first season in Colorado and followed up with another triumph five years later.

The team was welcomed to Denver with open arms just over a quarter of a century ago and was quickly nicknamed "the

Avs." They have been one of the most consistently entertaining teams in the league ever since, just as the Nordiques were.

The franchise has featured several players who are now in the Hockey Hall of Fame, such as Ray Bourque, Guy Lafleur, Peter Forsberg, Rob Blake, and Joe Sakic. And who could forget Patrick Roy, possibly the greatest goaltender of all time and former Avs head coach?

This trivia-fact book contains a wide variety of information about the Avalanche franchise, beginning in 1979 when it made its NHL debut to the conclusion of the 2019-20 regular NHL season.

The book is divided into 15 chapters; each has a specific topic. Each section offers 20 multiple-choice and true-false questions, with the correct answers following on a separate page. The chapters also feature 10 interesting "Did You Know?" facts and anecdotes regarding the franchise.

For Avalanche fans, this is a tremendous way to re-live the ups and downs of the club and perhaps learn a few things about its days in Quebec at the same time. The book will help you challenge fellow fans in trivia contests, as well as friends and family members.

The Avs haven't won the Stanley Cup for a couple of decades now, but their fans are delighted with the direction the team's going in and with the bright young stars suiting up night after night.

Hopefully, this book will remind you why you're such a loyal Avalanche supporter.

# CHAPTER 1:

# ORIGINS & HISTORY

## QUIZ TIME!

1. What team was the Colorado Avalanche before being relocated?

    a. Winnipeg Jets
    b. Cleveland Barons
    c. Kansas City Scouts
    d. Quebec Nordiques

2. When did the franchise play its first NHL season?

    a. 1972-73
    b. 1976-77
    c. 1995-96
    d. 1979-80

3. Who was the first coach of the Avalanche?

    a. Bob Hartley
    b. Marc Crawford
    c. Pierre Page
    d. Dave Chambers

4. Colorado's first NHL team was the Colorado Rockies.

    a. True
    b. False

5. How many points did the Avalanche record in their first season?

    a. 100
    b. 95
    c. 104
    d. 107

6. Who scored the first goal for the re-branded Avalanche?

    a. Craig Wolanin
    b. Scott Young
    c. Claude Lemieux
    d. Valeri Kamensky

7. The Avs won their first game against which team?

    a. New York Islanders
    b. Detroit Red Wings
    c. Toronto Maple Leafs
    d. Florida Panthers

8. The Avalanche won their first Stanley Cup in their inaugural season.

    a. True
    b. False

9. Which company bought the rights to bring a team to Denver?

a. ABC

b. NJSEA

c. COMSAT

d. NASDAQ

10. What name was not considered when re-branding the team?

   a. Black Bears

   b. Sasquatch

   c. Extreme

   d. Blizzards

11. The Avalanche won 47 games in their first NHL season.

   a. True

   b. False

12. Who did Colorado defeat in the Finals to win their first Stanley Cup?

   a. New Jersey Devils

   b. Washington Capitals

   c. Florida Panthers

   d. New York Rangers

13. The Avalanche played their first three seasons in which division?

   a. Central

   b. Northwest

   c. Northeast

   d. Pacific

14. From 1995 to 1999, the Avs played their home games at McNichols Sports Arena.

    a. True
    b. False

15. The Avalanche made the playoffs for how many consecutive seasons after moving to Colorado?

    a. 11
    b. 10
    c. 7
    d. 9

16. How many coaches did the Avalanche have in their first 10 years?

    a. 2
    b. 4
    c. 5
    d. 3

17. On what date did Colorado play its first game at the Pepsi Center in 1999?

    a. November 1
    b. October 15
    c. October 20
    d. October 13

18. Who was the first player to skate onto the ice at the Avs' home opener in 1995?

    a. Stéphane Fiset
    b. Joe Sakic

c. Adam Foote

d. Jocelyn Thibault

19. How many games did the Avalanche lose in their first season?

    a. 24

    b. 30

    c. 25

    d. 18

20. The Avalanche recorded five shutouts in their inaugural season.

    a. True

    b. False

# QUIZ ANSWERS

1. D – Quebec Nordiques

2. C – 1995-96

3. B – Marc Crawford

4. A – True

5. C – 104

6. D – Valeri Kamensky

7. B – Detroit Red Wings

8. A – True

9. C – COMSAT

10. B – Sasquatch

11. A – True

12. C – Florida Panthers

13. D – Pacific

14. A – True

15. B – 10

16. B – 4

17. D – October 13

18. A – Stéphane Fiset

19. C – 25

20. B – False

# DID YOU KNOW?

1. The Colorado Avalanche is based in Denver, Colorado, and play in the Central Division of the NHL's Western Conference. The franchise joined the NHL as the Quebec Nordiques in 1979 and moved to Denver before the start of the 1995-96 season. The club is owned by Ann Walton Kroenke.

2. The Avalanche play their home games at the Pepsi Center in Denver and share the facility with the Denver Nuggets of the National Basketball Association (NBA). The team has two minor-league affiliates, the Colorado Eagles of the American Hockey League (AHL) and the Utah Grizzlies of the East Coast Hockey League (ECHL).

3. The Quebec Nordiques were founded in 1972 when the franchise was in the now-defunct World Hockey Association (WHA). The club joined the NHL when four WHA teams, the Nordiques, Edmonton Oilers, New England Whalers, and Winnipeg Jets, merged into the NHL. Colorado had previously hosted the Colorado Rockies NHL team from 1976 to 1982 before they relocated to New Jersey.

4. The Nordiques were originally meant to play in San Francisco, when the ownership group was awarded a franchise there. However, the club hit a roadblock concerning finances and a place to play and soon found

9

itself in Quebec City. In seven seasons in the WHA, the team won the Avco World Trophy in 1976-77 after losing in the final in 1974-75.

5. The Nordiques made the playoffs seven straight years from 1980-81 to 1986-87 but then went downhill. They finished in the basement of their division every season from 1987-88 to 1991-92, and in three of those five seasons, they finished last in the NHL. Their worst campaign came in 1989-90, when they won just 12 games for a franchise low.

6. In their first NHL campaign in Colorado, the franchise topped the Pacific Division and went on to defeat the Florida Panthers in four games to win the Stanley Cup. In doing so, the Avalanche became the first franchise to capture the Stanley Cup the first season after relocating. It was also the first major North American professional sports championship won by a Denver-based club.

7. The franchise won its second Stanley Cup in 2000-01 when they edged the New Jersey Devils in seven games in the Final. This means the Avalanche are currently the only active NHL franchise to be undefeated in their Stanley Cup Finals appearances.

8. Colorado has hoisted the division title nine times in team history. This includes eight consecutive times after the team relocated to Denver. Eight straight division championships is an NHL record, and the team made the playoffs in the first 10 seasons after moving to Denver. The postseason streak came to a halt in 1973-74.

9. The Nordiques struggled financially in Quebec because it was the NHL's smallest market at the time. Then-owner Marcel Aubut sought help from the province's government in 1995 and also wanted taxpayers to fund a new arena. When these plans fell through, he sold the team to Denver's COMSAT Entertainment Group, which owned the Denver Nuggets of the NBA and was operated by Charlie Lyons. The deal was sealed on July 1, 1995, and the club headed straight to Colorado.

10. The franchise's current owner, Ann Walton Kroenke, is an heir to the Walmart fortune and also the owner of the NBA's Denver Nuggets. In addition, her husband Stan Kroenke is the majority owner of the Los Angeles Rams of the National Football League (NFL), the Colorado Rapids of Major League Soccer (MLS), the Colorado Mammoth of the National Lacrosse League (NLL), and the soccer team Arsenal of the English Premier League.

# CHAPTER 2:

# JERSEYS & NUMBERS

## QUIZ TIME!

1. How many jersey numbers were retired by the Nordiques?

    a. 3

    b. 6

    c. 4

    d. 5

2. How many numbers have the Avalanche retired?

    a. 5

    b. 7

    c. 6

    d. 4

3. In 2015, the Avs introduced an alternate jersey with an updated version of the old Colorado Rockies logo.

    a. True

    b. False

4. The Avalanche wore a shoulder crest with an image of what until 2015?

   a. Altered C from the Colorado state flag
   b. Sasquatch foot
   c. Mountain peak
   d. Sasquatch head

5. Which player had his number retired by the Avalanche in 2001?

   a. Peter Forsberg
   b. Joe Sakic
   c. Ray Bourque
   d. Patrick Roy

6. Valeri Kamensky wore which number as a member of the Avalanche?

   a. 14
   b. 12
   c. 15
   d. 13

7. Which number was not retired by the Nordiques?

   a. 3
   b. 23
   c. 8
   d. 26

8. Colorado's home jersey color is a shade of mahogany.

   a. True
   b. False

9. As of 2019-20, how many Avalanche and Nordiques players have worn number 28?

    a. 28

    b. 25

    c. 27

    d. 30

10. Before switching to number 19, what number did Joe Sakic wear in his first NHL season?

    a. 18

    b. 20

    c. 87

    d. 88

11. Adam Foote was the only franchise player to wear number 52.

    a. True

    b. False

12. Who wore number 19 for nine seasons before Joe Sakic?

    a. Alain Cote

    b. Michel Dion

    c. Mike Natyshak

    d. Anton Stastny

13. As of 2019-20, how many Avalanche jerseys have been made for special event games?

    a. 1

    b. 4

    c. 2

    d. 3

14. Paul Stastny was the last player to wear number 26 for the franchise.

    a. True
    b. False

15. Who was the first player to wear number 81 for the Avs?

    a. Joonas Donskoi
    b. Matthew Nieto
    c. Vladislav Kamenev
    d. Tomas Vincour

16. Who wore number 1 from 2012 to 2019?

    a. Spencer Martin
    b. Calvin Pickard
    c. Semyon Varlamov
    d. Peter Budaj

17. Before the Nordiques moved to Colorado, they planned to change their logo to what snowy animal?

    a. Polar bear
    b. Siberian husky
    c. Wolf
    d. Arctic fox

18. When did the Avalanche introduce an alternate jersey?

    a. 1999-2000
    b. 2002-03
    c. 2000-01
    d. 2001-02

19. Which Nordiques player was the first to have their number retired?

   a. J.C. Tremblay
   b. Peter Stastny
   c. Marc Tardif
   d. Michel Goulet

20. The Avalanche's primary jerseys have remained relatively unchanged from 1995 to 2020.

   a. True
   b. False

# QUIZ ANSWERS

1.  C – 4
2.  C – 6
3.  A – True
4.  B – Sasquatch foot
5.  C – Ray Bourque
6.  D – 13
7.  B – 23
8.  B – False
9.  C – 27
10. D – 88
11. A – True
12. A – Alain Cote
13. C – 2
14. B – False
15. D – Tomas Vincour
16. C – Semyon Varlamov
17. B – Siberian husky
18. D – 2001-02
19. A – J.C. Tremblay
20. A – True

# DID YOU KNOW?

1. The Avalanche's jerseys are predominantly burgundy and dark blue with silver trimming and white with burgundy. They also wear black pants with their regular home and away uniforms. There is also a steel blue alternate or third jersey, and special edition uniforms have been worn on occasions such as the 2020 NHL Stadium Series.

2. The team's logo consists of a burgundy-colored letter A which has snow wrapped around it to give the impression of an avalanche shaped like the letter C. In addition, a hockey puck can be found in the lower right section of the snow, and there is a blue oval on the background.

3. Colorado's original alternate logo featured the foot of a Sasquatch or Big Foot creature and was placed on the shoulders of the jersey. This was used from 1995 to 2015. The new alternate logo, which contains the Colorado state flag's insignia in the team's colors, was introduced for the 20-year anniversary campaign in 2015-16.

4. The Avalanche has so far retired six jersey numbers. These are forwards Joe Sakic (19), Peter Forsberg (21), and Milan Hejduk (23); goaltender Patrick Roy (33); and defenders Adam Foote (52) and Ray Bourque (77). Sakic, Forsberg, Bourque, and Roy are also in the Hockey Hall of Fame.

5. When the franchise was located in Quebec, the Nordiques retired four numbers. They belonged to defender J.C.

Tremblay (3) and forwards Marc Tardif (8), Michel Goulet (16), and Peter Stastny (26). The NHL also retired Wayne Gretzky's number 99.

6.  The numbers retired by the Nordiques were put back into circulation when the franchise relocated in Colorado. As of 2019-20, seven players had worn number 3, while eight players have also worn number 8, and seven have donned number 16. A total of four players have worn number 26, including Peter Stastny's son Paul Stastny.

7.  The most popular number in franchise history so far has been 17, as 28 different players have worn it, including Pat Hickey, Bran Lawton, Wendel Clark, Jari Kurri, and Tyson Jost. Number 28 is a close second, with 27 players wearing it. These include Andre Dupont, Steve Duchesne, Eric Lacroix, and Ian Cole.

8.  The lowest number worn in the franchise's history has been 1, which has been donned by a dozen different goaltenders. The highest number worn was 97, which Per Ledin wore on his back in 2009.

9.  Each number from 1 to 65 has been worn by at least one player of the Nordiques and Avalanche. In addition, 17 numbers between 71 and 97 have been taken at least once. The numbers 71, 81, 90, 91, and 92 have been worn by two players, while three players have donned number 88.

10. The number 13, which some superstitious people consider to be unlucky, has been worn by six different players in Avalanche-Nordiques history. Those who had

no fear of it have been Mats Sundin, Valeri Kamensky, Dan Hinote, Freddie Hamilton, Alexander Kerfoot, and Valeri Nichushkin.

# CHAPTER 3:

# FAMOUS QUOTES

## QUIZ TIME!

1. Which goalie was Derick Brassard referring to when he said, "We know this team, they ran with two goalies all season long. He's beatable, he is a good goalie, but we can find a way to pass some pucks through him."?

    a. Cam Talbot
    b. Mike Smith
    c. Martin Jones
    d. Aaron Dell

2. Joe Sakic had this to say after losing which player to free agency in 2014-15: "I respect him for everything he has done for the Avalanche. It was his right, and he is going home."?

    a. David Van der Gulik
    b. Brad Malone
    c. Paul Stastny
    d. Matt Hunwick

3. Coach Jared Bednar said this about rookie Tyson Jost: "It is great to see him have success because I think success breeds success."

   a. True
   b. False

4. Which player said this about his retirement: "I always said to myself that the minute I thought I'd slipped and wasn't the player I wanted to be, it was time for me to go."?

   a. Joe Sakic
   b. Jarome Iginla
   c. Ray Bourque
   d. Patrick Roy

5. Which player complimented Avs fans in 2018 by saying, "The fan support has been awesome all year. I think you guys have seen it."?

   a. Gabriel Landeskog
   b. Nathan MacKinnon
   c. Semyon Varlamov
   d. Mikko Rantanen

6. "I wanted to keep playing in Denver for a long time" was said by which former player?

   a. Peter Forsberg
   b. Ryan O'Reilly
   c. Tyson Barrie
   d. Milan Hejduk

7. Which player said this about the Avs' chances of winning the Stanley Cup: "I really haven't had this feeling since I was in junior, of really believing you can win. I think it elevates everybody's game."?

    a. Martin Kaut
    b. J.T. Compher
    c. Nathan MacKinnon
    d. Cale Makar

8. After scoring his first NHL goal, defender Patrick Nemeth said, "I think, first off, my role here is to play solid defense and get the puck out of our zone and if I score it's great and if not, hopefully I am doing my other job well."

    a. True
    b. False

9. This Avs player had this to say about the team's determination: "We have to approach every game as if it was a playoff game and we need to win every single one of them."?

    a. Peter Forsberg
    b. Alex Tanguay
    c. Gabriel Landeskog
    d. Adam Foote

10. When finding out he had been traded, who said, "I kind of knew before they told me. I saw them talking on the bench. It was very strange but I kind of half-expected it."?

    a. Kyle Turris
    b. Peter Forsberg

c.  Matt Duchene

d.  Jarome Iginla

11. Detroit Red Wings player Darren McCarty remarked, "I cold-cocked him," about the time he punched the Avs' Claude Lemieux.

a.  True

b.  False

12. Which Avs coach repeatedly shouted, "Are you gonna apologize?" during an infamous shouting match with Detroit Red Wings coach Scotty Bowman?

a.  Tony Granato

b.  Pierre Page

c.  Bob Hartley

d.  Marc Crawford

13. Who said, "But I want stability. If we don't come to an agreement, I will play for CSKA," when discussing contract negotiations in 2017?

a.  Andrei Mironov

b.  Fedor Tyutin

c.  Nikita Zadorov

d.  Mikhail Grigorenko

14. In 2014-15, Matt Duchene remarked, "When I get over the blue line, if I don't have a chance to score, I'm not shooting it. I'm going to hold on and try to make a play."

a.  True

b.  False

15. Who simply stated, "Somebody was in front and made the defenseman concentrate on someone else... I just whacked at it and it went in."?

    a. Alexander Kerfoot
    b. Adam Foote
    c. Adam Deadmarsh
    d. Paul Stastny

16. After a 5-3 win over Carolina in 2017, which goalie commented, "You know, when you score five goals, you can give up three and it's easy to play that way."?

    a. Jonathan Bernier
    b. Semyon Varlamov
    c. Andrew Hammond
    d. Calvin Pickard

17. Which player described Nathan MacKinnon's game in 2020 by saying, "If he's not in his prime now, I mean, what's he going to score when he is, 170 points? He's on pace for about 120 now."?

    a. Erik Johnson
    b. Tyson Jost
    c. Nikita Zadorov
    d. Ian Cole

18. Which Avs player famously responded with this comment after being insulted by Jeremy Roenick in the playoffs: "I didn't hear him because my two Stanley Cup rings were plugging my ears."?

a. Peter Forsberg

b. David Aebischer

c. Patrick Roy

d. Adam Foote

19. Which coach made this comment about Colorado's playoff ability: "I think there are some things that we weren't doing. I didn't think we had a shot mentality. It's a reflection of our 5-on-5 play too."?

a. Patrick Roy

b. Joel Quenneville

c. Joe Sacco

d. Jared Bednar

20. In 2018, Nathan MacKinnon said this about the team's locker room chemistry: "I think it tells the story about our locker room and our character. It wasn't the first time we were down in the third period and still, found a way to win."

a. True

b. False

# QUIZ ANSWERS

1. B – Mike Smith

2. C – Paul Stastny

3. B – False

4. A – Joe Sakic

5. A – Gabriel Landeskog

6. D – Milan Hejduk

7. C – Nathan MacKinnon

8. A – True

9. B – Alex Tanguay

10. C – Matt Duchene

11. A – True

12. D – Marc Crawford

13. C – Nikita Zadorov

14. A – True

15. B – Adam Foote

16. B – Semyon Varlamov

17. A – Erik Johnson

18. C – Patrick Roy

19. D – Jared Bednar

20. B – False

# DID YOU KNOW?

1.  On reminiscing about the franchise's days in Quebec, Joe Sakic said, "Quebec City will always be a special place for me, as I started my career there and the fans are great hockey fans. But mostly all I knew as a player there was losing. That all changed when the franchise relocated to Denver and became known as the Colorado Avalanche."

2.  "I try to hit everybody as hard as I can, just like everybody tries to hit me as hard as they can. At worst, I thought it should have been a two-minute penalty but then the referee saw blood and decided to change his mind." Colorado forward Claude Lemieux's words after receiving a major match penalty and two-game suspension following a 1996 hit from behind on Detroit's Kris Draper that resulted in reconstructive facial surgery.

3.  After seeing his teammate Draper's face following the hit by Lemieux, Detroit forward Dino Ciccarelli remarked, "I can't believe I shook his frigging hand," after the two teams shook hands following the game, which won the playoff series for Colorado.

4.  Former Avalanche goaltender and head coach Patrick Roy had this to say about Hall-of-Famer Mario Lemieux: "Usually when you play a team, you want to focus on one line. Pittsburgh is the only team where you have to focus on one player, Mario Lemieux. When he's coming toward you, all you see is him."

5.  In March 1999, Colorado fought back from a 5-0 deficit to Florida to earn a 7-5 win with Peter Forsberg tallying six points in the final 22 minutes of the game. After the comeback, he remarked, "It all kept happening so fast. It started to feel like nothing could go wrong but I remember thinking this game is over after it got to 5-0."

6.  When Denver sportswriter Adrian Dater was asked to cover the NBA's Denver Nuggets instead of the Avalanche in 2003-04, he agreed but then changed his mind after the hockey team signed free agent forwards Teemu Selanne and Paul Kariya. He commented, "I was convinced if I didn't I would be turning down a chance at covering maybe the greatest NHL team of all time."

7.  Following a 7-0 humiliation in Detroit in March 1996, the team drowned its sorrows at a local bar. Head coach Marc Crawford recalled the events of the next day by saying, "We got plastered, all of us. I don't think any of us were feeling too good the next morning. I think a lot of us were a little shaky on our skates."

8.  Avalanche television broadcaster Peter McNab once told his colleagues on air: "Guys, I was sitting beside captain Gabriel Landeskog at the rink yesterday, and he took his shirt off and it was like chiseled granite, it was just ridiculous."

9.  Former Colorado blueliner Ray Bourque once said, "If I can be half the hockey player that Bobby Orr was, I'll be happy." Bourque currently holds the NHL records for

most career goals, assists, and points by a defender, won the James Norris Memorial Trophy five times, is a Hall-of-Famer, and earned a spot on the league's end-of-season All-Star teams 19 times.

10. When the franchise was situated in Quebec and drafted Eric Lindros 1st overall in 1991, the future Hall of Fame center refused to play with the team. He later explained the reason by remarking, "The decision to not play for Quebec was based solely on the owner (Marcel Aubut). It had nothing to do with language, culture, or city. Keep in mind, my wife is from Quebec. I was not going to play for that individual—period."

# CHAPTER 4:

## CATCHY NICKNAMES

1. Quiz Time!

   a. What was Ryan O'Reilly's nickname in Colorado?
   b. Odd Ball
   c. Dragon
   d. Factor
   e. The O-Dominator

2. Which is not one of Joe Sakic's nicknames?

   a. Burnaby Joe
   b. Mr. Clutch
   c. Go-Go Joe
   d. Super Joe

3. Jarome Iginla's nickname was simply "Iggy."

   a. True
   b. False

4. Peter Forsberg was also known by which nickname?

   a. The Prince
   b. Meatballs
   c. The Great
   d. The King

5. Former Avs netminder Peter Budaj was nicknamed after which cartoon character?

   a. Peter Rabbit
   b. Ned Flanders
   c. Peter Griffin
   d. Daffy Duck

6. Gabriel Landeskog also goes by which nickname?

   a. Landy
   b. Gabe
   c. Landlord
   d. Gabby

7. What is NOT one of the nicknames for the Avalanche?

   a. The Snowy A
   b. 'Lanches
   c. The Altitude
   d. Avs

8. Patrick Roy was dubbed "St. Patrick."

   a. True
   b. False

9. Who was known as "The Razor"?

   a. Alex Tanguay
   b. Milan Hejduk
   c. Ryan Smyth
   d. Andrew Raycroft

10. Which Avs player was known as "The Finnish Flash"?

    a. Antti Laaksonen

    b. Ossi Väänänen

    c. Riku Hahl

    d. Teemu Selanne

11. Goaltender Andrew Hammond was known as "The Hamburglar."

    a. True

    b. False

12. Which is NOT one of Erik Johnson's nicknames?

    a. E.J.

    b. Condor

    c. Judge

    d. Edge

13. What is Matthew Nieto's nickname?

    a. Tito

    b. Nemo

    c. Matty

    d. Big Toe

14. Kurt Sauer was called "Soda" while in Colorado.

    a. True

    b. False

15. Which goaltender was nicknamed "Donut"?

    a. Semyon Varlamov

    b. Jose Theodore

c. David Aebischer

d. Jean-Sébastien Giguère

16. What do Nathan MacKinnon's teammates call him?

    a. Mack Truck

    b. King Mack

    c. MacK

    d. Big Mack

17. Mikko Rantanen goes by which of the following nicknames?

    a. The Critic

    b. The Tan Finn

    c. Rags

    d. Hot Wheels

18. Milan Hejduk had what royal moniker?

    a. The Czech Prince

    b. The Duke

    c. Milan the Marquess

    d. The Baron

19. What nickname did Alex Tanguay go by during his playing career?

    a. Hot Sauce

    b. Tangerine

    c. Tangs

    d. Tonic

20. Sven Andrighetto was simply called "Ghetto" while in Colorado.

    a. True

    b. False

# QUIZ ANSWERS

1. C – Factor

2. C – Go-Go Joe

3. A – True

4. C – The Great

5. B – Ned Flanders

6. A – Landy

7. C – The Altitude

8. A – True

9. D – Andrew Raycroft

10. D – Teemu Selanne

11. A – True

12. C – Judge

13. B – Nemo

14. B – False

15. A – Semyon Varlamov

16. C – MacK

17. D – Hot Wheels

18. B – The Duke

19. C – Tangs

20. A – True

# DID YOU KNOW?

1. The City of Denver is commonly known by its nickname the "Mile High City" because its official elevation is a mile above sea level. The state of Colorado is known as the "Centennial State" because it became a state in the year 1876, which was 100 years after America's Declaration of Independence. It's sometimes known as "Colorful Colorado" as well. As for the Avalanche franchise itself, the club is simply referred to by most fans as "the Avs."

2. Former goaltender and head coach Patrick Roy was simply known as "Saint Patrick." He split his playing career between Montreal and Colorado and won two Stanley Cups with each franchise. The Hall-of-Famer is the only NHL player to win the Conn Smythe Trophy three times as MVP of the playoffs. He's also the only one to win it in different decades and capture it for two different teams.

3. Joe Sakic had several nicknames during his NHL career, including "Burnaby Joe," "Super Joe," and "Mr. Clutch." The "Burnaby Joe" nickname was usually used by residents of the Canadian province of British Columbia since he was born there in the city of Burnaby. He earned the "Mr. Clutch" name for his eight career overtime goals in the playoffs.

4. Wade Belak was known as one of the toughest players in the NHL and went by the nickname "The Intimidator" due to his rugged style of play. He was assessed 1,263

penalty minutes in 549 regular-season games during his NHL career and played with the Avs from 1996-97 to 1998-99. Sadly, Belak died at the age of 35 in August 2011.

5. Since he often had a painting of the Ned Flanders character from *The Simpsons* television show on his mask, goaltender Peter Budaj was known as "Ned Flanders" as well as monikers such as "Buddy," "Buds," and "Buddha." He played with Colorado from 2005 to 2011, and in 2011, he became the first Slovakian-born goaltender to win 100 NHL games.

6. After winning the Stanley Cup with the Washington Capitals in 2017-18, forward André Burakovsky was traded to Colorado in June 2019. He signed a one-year deal and notched 20 goals and 45 points in 58 games in 2019-20. His nicknames with the team are "Barracuda" and "Burkie."

7. Power forward Wendel Clark's days with the franchise were spent as a Quebec Nordique in 1994-95. Clark was known as "Captain Crunch" due to the bone-jarring body checks he was known to deliver. His rivals and their fans had another nickname for him though, which was "Wendy."

8. Forward Joseph Taylor Compher is commonly known as J.T. Compher. However, his nicknames with the Avs are "Jimothy Timothy" and "Jompher Compher." He broke into the NHL with Colorado in 2016-17 and had 43 goals and 91 points at the end of the 2019-20 season. He signed a

four-year contract extension with the team in July 2019 for $14 million.

9.  Another player known for his physical style of play was Andre Dupont, who was known throughout the hockey world as "Moose." The blueliner earned the moniker with the "Broad Street Bullies" of Philadelphia. He then finished his career from 1980 to 1983 with Quebec. "Moose" served 1,986 penalty minutes in his 800-game NHL career and is a former Nordiques captain.

10. Winger Ian Laperrière's nicknames were "Mumbles," "Lappy," and "The Sparkplug." He played with Colorado from 2005 to 2009 and made franchise history on April 1, 2009, when he fought David Hale of the Phoenix Coyotes. That was the 52nd fight for Laperrière in a Colorado jersey, which passed Scott Parker for the most fighting majors in the organization's history.

# CHAPTER 5:

# THE CAPTAIN CLASS

## QUIZ TIME!

1. Who was named Avs captain in 2012-13?

    a. Nathan MacKinnon

    b. Gabriel Landeskog

    c. Erik Johnson

    d. Matthew Nieto

2. As of 2020, how many players have held the Colorado captaincy?

    a. 3

    b. 7

    c. 5

    d. 4

3. Joe Sakic was the last captain of the Quebec Nordiques and first captain of the Colorado Avalanche.

    a. True

    b. False

4. Who became the Avs' captain after Joe Sakic retired?

    a. Paul Stastny
    b. Ruslan Salei
    c. Adam Foote
    d. Milan Hejduk

5. At what age did Gabriel Landeskog become Avalanche captain?

    a. 21
    b. 22
    c. 20
    d. 19

6. Who was the first captain of the Quebec Nordiques?

    a. Andre Dupont
    b. Robbie Ftorek
    c. Mario Marois
    d. Marc Tardif

7. What is the most penalty minutes recorded by an Avs captain in one season?

    a. 79
    b. 103
    c. 84
    d. 62

8. Guy Lafleur was once the Nordiques' captain.

    a. True
    b. False

9. How many captains did the Nordiques have while in the NHL?

    a. 9
    b. 4
    c. 8
    d. 6

10. What is the fewest games played by a captain in a single season for the Avalanche as of 2019-20?

    a. 30
    b. 22
    c. 8
    d. 15

11. Adam Foote was the Avalanche's oldest captain at 40 years old.

    a. True
    b. False

12. In 1990-91, captain Steven Finn recorded how many penalty minutes with Quebec?

    a. 252
    b. 140
    c. 228
    d. 169

13. What is the best plus/minus recorded by an Avs captain as of 2019-20?

    a. +45
    b. +67

c. +50

d. +38

14. In 1990-91, Steven Finn and Joe Sakic were co-captains of Quebec.

    a. True
    b. False

15. What is the most points a Nordiques captain recorded in a single season?

    a. 98
    b. 107
    c. 119
    d. 122

16. In 2011-12, Milan Hejduk recorded the lowest penalty minutes in a season by a Colorado captain with at least 80 games played. How many did he receive?

    a. 6
    b. 14
    c. 10
    d. 18

17. For how many seasons was Peter Stastny captain of the Nordiques?

    a. 4
    b. 5
    c. 6
    d. 7

18. What is the lowest plus/minus an Avs captain has recorded as of 2019-20?

    a. -43
    b. -29
    c. -25
    d. -30

19. For how many seasons was Joe Sakic captain of Colorado?

    a. 16
    b. 15
    c. 14
    d. 13

20. Milan Hejduk captained the Avs for only one season.

    a. True
    b. False

# QUIZ ANSWERS

1.  B – Gabriel Landeskog

2.  D – 4

3.  A – True

4.  C – Adam Foote

5.  D – 19

6.  D – Marc Tardif

7.  A – 79

8.  B – False

9.  C – 8

10. D – 15

11. B – False

12. C – 228

13. A – +45

14. A – True

15. D – 122

16. B – 14

17. B – 5

18. C – -25

19. D – 13

20. A – True

# DID YOU KNOW?

1. Since moving to Colorado, the franchise has had just four captains. They are Joe Sakic, Adam Foote, Milan Hejduk, and Gabriel Landeskog. Sakic was the captain when the club arrived in Denver from Quebec and held the job until 2009. Foote wore the C for the next two seasons and Hejduk for one season. Landeskog was then appointed captain in 2012-13.

2. All told, the franchise has had 11 different captains. Those who held the position with Quebec were Marc Tardif, Andre "Moose" Dupont, Robbie Ftorek, Mario Marois, Peter Stastny, Joe Sakic, Steven Finn, and Mike Hough. Sakic was co-captain in 1990-91 with Finn, and then Hough took over in 1991-92. Sakic was then re-appointed captain in 1992-93.

3. Forward Gabriel Landeskog was the youngest captain in the franchise's history at just 19 years and 286 days old when given the honor in 2012. This made him the NHL's youngest captain ever at the time. The oldest captains were Sakic and Adam Foote. Sakic was 39 in 2008-09, and Foote was the same age in 2010-11.

4. The longest-serving captain was Joe Sakic, who wore the C for 17 seasons, with 16 of them being consecutive. He started as captain in Quebec and finished as captain in Colorado. The shortest reign was Robbie Ftorek's 19-game stint in 1981-82.

5. The most physical captain was Steven Finn in 1990-91, when the defenseman served 228 minutes in penalties with Quebec. He also chipped in with 3 goals and 19 points in 71 games that season. Finn served 1,514 minutes in penalties with the team in 605 regular-season games until 1995.

6. The best point-scoring season by a captain of the franchise came in 1985-86, when center Peter Stastny racked up 41 goals and 81 assists for 122 points in 76 games with Quebec. Joe Sakic wasn't far off the mark in 1995-96 in Colorado, when he posted 51 goals and 69 assists for 120 points in 82 contests.

7. Left winger Marc Tardif was Quebec's captain from 1979 to 1981, when the franchise joined the NHL from the WHA. He then stayed another two seasons in Quebec and notched 244 points in 272 regular-season outings. Tardif was a star in the WHA; he led the league in goals, assists, and points twice and was the league's all-time top goal-getter with 316. Quebec acquired him from the Montreal Canadiens in the 1979 NHL Expansion Draft.

8. Robbie Ftorek was another former WHA star who played the first two seasons with Quebec when the team joined the NHL. He was captain for 19 games in 1981-82 before being traded to the New York Rangers. Although just 155 pounds, Ftorek was feisty and served 104 penalty minutes in 1980-81. He tallied 133 points in 149 games with the Nordiques after signing as a free agent.

9.  Quebec's captain from 1982 to 1985 was Mario Marois before Peter Stastny took over. The defender was acquired via a trade with Vancouver in March 1981 and was then traded to Winnipeg in November 1985. Winnipeg traded Marois back to Quebec three years later, and he stayed two seasons before St. Louis took him in the 1990 Waiver Draft. He posted 200 points in 401 regular-season games with Quebec.

10. Mike Hough was sole captain of the Nordiques in 1991-92 and contributed 16 goals and 38 points in 61 games that season. The left winger was drafted 181st overall by the team in 1982 and played 363 games with Quebec with 165 points to his name. Hough was then traded to Washington in June 1993.

# CHAPTER 6:

# STATISTICALLY SPEAKING

## QUIZ TIME!

1. The most goals scored in a season by an Avs player is?

    a. 56
    b. 60
    c. 54
    d. 57

2. How many power-play goals did Joe Sakic score in 2000-01 to set an Avalanche record?

    a. 20
    b. 28
    c. 29
    d. 19

3. The highest plus/minus recorded by a Colorado player is +52.

    a. True
    b. False

4. What was the most penalty minutes recorded in a season by a Nordiques player?

   a. 301
   b. 417
   c. 297
   d. 355

5. In the 2018-19 season, how many hits did the Avalanche deliver?

   a. 1,703
   b. 1,699
   c. 1,645
   d. 1,532

6. How many goals did Colorado score in its first season?

   a. 285
   b. 249
   c. 341
   d. 326

7. Colorado has attempted how many penalty shots as of 2019-20?

   a. 50
   b. 49
   c. 33
   d. 35

8. The Avs lost more faceoffs than they won in 2011-12.

   a. True
   b. False

9. How many hat tricks did the Nordiques score in team history?

    a. 97

    b. 101

    c. 59

    d. 73

10. As of 2019-20, the Avs have had how many seasons with 40-plus wins?

    a. 12

    b. 9

    c. 14

    d. 16

11. The final score of Colorado's first game and victory was 3-2.

    a. True

    b. False

12. Who is the Avalanche coach with the most wins?

    a. Marc Crawford

    b. Bob Hartley

    c. Jared Bednar

    d. Joel Quenneville

13. What is the highest goals-per-game average by a Colorado player in a season, recorded in 2000-01?

    a. 0.75

    b. 0.63

    c. 0.71

    d. 0.66

14. The most games played by a franchise goalie in a single, regular season is 73.

    a. True

    b. False

15. Peter Forsberg has the highest assists per game in a season for the Avalanche. What is it?

    a. 1.03

    b. 0.95

    c. 1.07

    d. 0.92

16. In Colorado's first season, how many shutouts did the team post?

    a. 1

    b. 4

    c. 2

    d. 5

17. Who led the team with 365 shots on goal in 2018-19?

    a. Mikko Rantanen

    b. Nathan MacKinnon

    c. Gabriel Landeskog

    d. Tyson Barrie

18. How many goals did the Nordiques allow in their first NHL campaign?

    a. 210

    b. 302

    c. 248

    d. 313

19. How many times have the Avalanche scored on penalty shot attempts as of 2019-20?

    a. 15
    b. 22
    c. 8
    d. 13

20. In Colorado's first season, their netminders made 2,130 saves.

    a. True
    b. False

# QUIZ ANSWERS

1. C – 54

2. D – 19

3. A – True

4. A – 301

5. B – 1,699

6. D – 326

7. C – 33

8. B – False

9. A – 97

10. D – 16

11. A – True

12. B – Bob Hartley

13. D – 0.66

14. B – False

15. A – 1.03

16. C – 2

17. B – Nathan MacKinnon

18. D – 313

19. D – 13

20. A – True

# DID YOU KNOW?

1. The most points Quebec earned in an NHL season was 104 in 1992-93, with a record of 47-27-10. This set a club record for the most wins while in the NHL. However, they did have fewer losses in 1994-95 with a record of 30-13-5 when the season was shortened to 48 games due to an NHL lockout. The team's all-time NHL record was 792-836-184 for 1,768 points in 1,812 games.

2. Colorado's most successful regular season was 2000-01 with 118 points on a record of 52-16-10. This set the franchise record for wins in an NHL season, which was equaled in 2013-14. The 16 defeats was a club low for an NHL season with over 48 games played. The lowest point total for an Avalanche campaign was 2012-13, when they earned 39 in another 48-game season. They posted just 48 points in 2016-17 with a record of 22-56-4, which is the most games Colorado has lost in a season.

3. Quebec's winning percentage peaked at .677 in 1994-95 in the shortened NHL season, while their worst was .194 in 1989-90 with a woeful mark of 12-61-7 for 31 points. The 12 wins is a NHL franchise low, while the 61 defeats is a franchise high. In Colorado, the 2000-01 campaign saw the team register a .720 winning percentage. Their lowest percentage was .293 in 2016-17.

4. In 16 NHL seasons, the Nordiques made the playoffs nine times. This included seven years in a row from 1980-81 to

1986-87. They then failed to make the postseason the next five years. As the Avalanche, the club has made the postseason 15 times as of the conclusion of the 2018-19 season. This includes 10 years in a row after arriving in Colorado in 1995-96. They then made the postseason just three times in the next 11 seasons.

5.  The combined Quebec-Colorado regular-season record (wins-losses-ties-overtime losses) stood at 1465-1314-261-138 at the conclusion of the 2019-20 regular season for 3,329 points. In the playoffs, the franchise record was 144-130 at the end of 2018-19, with two Stanley Cups as the Avalanche.

6.  The all-time point leader for the franchise is Joe Sakic with 1,641 in a club-high 1,378 regular-season games. Sakic is also first in goals with 625 and assists with 1,016. The former Quebec and Colorado captain also holds club records for the most goals and points in a playoff season, with 18 and 34, respectively, and the most overtime goals in the playoffs with eight.

7.  Sakic also holds career franchise highs in the regular season for game-winning goals at 86, power-play markers at 205, and shorthanded tallies at 32. His 388 even-strength goals and 4,621 shots on net are franchise records, and he was on the ice for a team-high 965 power-play goals, 2,220 total goals scored, and 1,527 total goals against.

8.  The most goals scored in a regular season was 57 by Michel Goulet in 1982-83, and his 29 power-play goals in

1987-88 is also a record. The most assists in a season was 93 and the most points in a campaign was 139 by center Peter Stastny in 1981-82. The most penalty minutes in a season was 301 by Gord Donnelly in 1987-88, while Dale Hunter served the most in his career with 1,562. All of these franchise records were set in Quebec.

9. Most of the franchise's regular-season goaltending records are held by Patrick Roy in Colorado. These include games played (478), wins (262), ties-overtime-shootout losses (65), goals against (1,070), shots against (12,994), saves (11,924), save percentage (.918), goals-against average (2.27), shutouts (37), and minutes (28,317). Semyon Varlamov of Colorado owns the record for most career losses, with 156.

10. As for single-season goaltending franchise records, Craig Anderson played the most games at 71, faced the most shots with 2,233, and recorded 2,047 saves; Semyon Varlamov won 41 games and posted the best save percentage at .927; Calvin Pickard lost 31 contests; Patrick Roy suffered 13 overtime-shootout defeats, posted the best goals-against average at 1.94 and nine shutouts. Dan Bouchard allowed a record 230 goals against in a season; his is the only one of these records that came in Quebec.

# CHAPTER 7:

# THE TRADE MARKET

## QUIZ TIME!

1. How many players did Colorado send to Montreal for Patrick Roy and Mike Keane?

    a. 2

    b. 4

    c. 5

    d. 3

2. How many trades did the Avs make in 2001-02?

    a. 5

    b. 13

    c. 7

    d. 10

3. The Avalanche acquired Claude Lemieux in a three-team trade.

    a. True

    b. False

4. What team did Colorado trade Sandis Ozoliňs to?

    a. Florida Panthers
    b. Carolina Hurricanes
    c. Mighty Ducks of Anaheim
    d. New York Rangers

5. Who did Colorado send to Los Angeles for Rob Blake and Steve Reinprecht?

    a. Aaron Miller and Brent Thompson
    b. Brent Thompson and a 1st round draft pick
    c. Adam Deadmarsh and a 1st round draft pick
    d. Adam Deadmarsh, Aaron Miller, and two 1st round draft picks

6. How many games did Jordan Leopold play for Colorado after being acquired from Calgary for Alex Tanguay?

    a. 122
    b. 91
    c. 65
    d. 213

7. What did Colorado give to Washington when trading for Philip Grubauer and Brooks Orpik in 2018-19?

    a. 2nd round draft pick in 2018
    b. Jean-Christophe Beaudin
    c. 3rd round draft pick in 2020
    d. Scott Kosmachuk

8. When the Avs traded Matt Duchene to Ottawa they received three players, three draft picks, and signing rights to a rookie prospect.

a. True

b. False

9. Which of these players was one of three acquired for Chris Drury and Stéphane Yelle in a 2002 trade with Calgary?

a. Chris McAllister

b. Bryan Marchment

c. Derek Morris

d. Dale Clark

10. Who did the Nordiques NOT receive in the blockbuster deal for Eric Lindros in 1992?

a. Kerry Huffman

b. Steve Duchesne

c. Mike Ricci

d. Mark Fitzpatrick

11. The Avs traded René Corbet, Wade Belak, and Robyn Regehr to Boston for Ray Bourque and Dave Andreychuk in 1999.

a. True

b. False

12. Which team did the Avalanche acquire Semyon Varlamov from on July 1, 2011?

a. Toronto Maple Leafs

b. San Jose Sharks

c. Washington Capitals

d. Tampa Bay Lightning

13. Who did Colorado trade Tom Gilbert for on March 9, 2004?

    a. Keith Ballard

    b. Jordan Krestanovich

    c. Matthew Barnaby

    d. Tommy Salo

14. Colorado traded David Jones and Shane O'Brien to Calgary for Alex Tanguay and Cory Sarich in 2013.

    a. True

    b. False

15. Who was NOT a part of the trade that brought Theo Fleury to Colorado?

    a. Michael Gaul

    b. Wade Belak

    c. Rene Corbet

    d. Chris Dingman

16. Which player did the Avs send with Ryan O'Reilly to the Buffalo Sabres?

    a. Stefan Elliot

    b. Marc-Andre Cliché

    c. Colin Smith

    d. Jamie McGinn

17. What did Colorado receive when they traded Jarome Iginla to the Los Angeles Kings?

    a. Felix Girard and a 6th round draft pick

    b. A 4th round draft pick

c. Rocco Grimaldi

d. A 3rd round draft pick

18. Who did the Avalanche send to the San Jose Sharks in exchange for Sandis Ozolinš?

a. Anson Carter

b. Claude Lapointe

c. Owen Nolan

d. John Slaney

19. Which player was NOT a part of the Patrick Roy deal in 1995?

a. Martin Ručinský

b. Steve Thomas

c. Andrei Kovalenko

d. Jocelyn Thibault

20. Colorado made 16 trades in 2003-04.

a. True

b. False

# QUIZ ANSWERS

1. D – 3
2. C – 7
3. A – True
4. B – Carolina Hurricanes
5. D – Adam Deadmarsh, Aaron Miller, and two 1st round draft picks
6. A – 122
7. A – 2nd round draft pick in 2018
8. A – True
9. C – Derek Morris
10. D – Mark Fitzpatrick
11. B – False
12. C – Washington Capitals
13. D – Tommy Salo
14. A – True
15. A – Michael Gaul
16. D – Jamie McGinn
17. B – A 4th round draft pick
18. C – Owen Nolan
19. B – Steve Thomas
20. A – True

# DID YOU KNOW?

1. One bad night for Montreal Canadiens goalie Patrick Roy in December 1995 helped turn the Avalanche franchise around. Roy was in net for Montreal's 11-1 home pounding by Detroit and allowed nine goals on 26 shots. When head coach Mario Tremblay finally pulled him in the second period, Roy told Montreal owner Ronald Corey he'd never play another game for the club. Roy was then suspended by the Habs and traded to Colorado four days later with captain Mike Keane for Jocelyn Thibault, Martin Ručinský, and Andrei Kovalenko.

2. After arriving in Colorado, Roy won the William M. Jennings Trophy and was named a First Team All-Star in 2001-02. He led Colorado to Stanley Cup triumphs in 1995-96 and 2000-01 and won the Conn Smythe Trophy as playoff MVP in 2000-01. The Avalanche retired his jersey, and Roy went on to coach the team and win the Jack Adams Award as coach of the year for 2013-14.

3. One of the franchise's biggest deals occurred in 1992 as the Nordiques. The club drafted center Eric Lindros 1st overall in 1991 even though he stated he wouldn't sign with the team. He sat out a year before being sent to Philadelphia for forwards Peter Forsberg and Mike Ricci, defensemen Steve Duchesne and Kerry Huffman, goaltender Ron Hextall, two 1st round draft picks, $15 million, and future considerations (Chris Simon).

4. Another blockbuster deal by Quebec saw center Mats Sundin, defender Garth Butcher, forward Todd Warriner, and the 10th overall draft pick go to Toronto for forward Wendel Clark, defender Sylvain Lefebvre, forward Landon Wilson, and the 22nd overall draft pick in 1994. Lefebvre would win a Stanley in Colorado, Sundin would go on to enjoy a Hall of Fame career, and Clark played only one season with Quebec.

5. After he held out for a better contract in 1998-99, Colorado traded offensive defenseman Sandis Ozolinš to Carolina in 2000 with a 2nd round draft pick for Nolan Pratt, a 1st round pick, which was used on Václav Nedorost, and two 2nd round picks, which became Agris Saviels and Jared Aulin. Pratt played just 46 games with the Avs before being traded, while Nedorost played only 67 games before being dealt. Aulin never played for Colorado, and Saviels never played an NHL game.

6. Blueliner Tyson Barrie, who posted 307 points in 484 games with Colorado, was sent to Toronto in July 2019 with forward Adam Kerfoot for center Nazem Kadri and rearguard Calle Rosen. Colorado also retained 50% of Barrie's salary for the final year of his deal. Colorado then sent Rosen back to Toronto at the 2019-20 trade deadline for backup goalie Michael Hutchinson. Barrie posted 39 points in 70 games with Toronto in 2019-20, while Kerfoot had 28 points in 65 contests. Kadri notched 19 goals and 36 points in 51 outings for the Avs.

7. One of Colorado's worst trades saw Chris Drury head to Calgary in 2003 with fellow forward and two-time Stanley Cup winner Stéphane Yelle for centers Derek Morris and Jeff Shantz and defender Dean McAmmond. Drury, the NHL's rookie of the year in 1998-99, scored at least 20 goals in his four seasons with the Avs and tallied 11 playoff goals in 2000-01 to help win the Stanley Cup. Colorado traded Morris in 2004, while McAmmond played in just 41 games before being swapped back to Calgary. Shantz played 79 games before leaving to play in Europe.

8. The Avalanche was involved in a three-way deal of forwards in October 1995, when they acquired Claude Lemieux. New Jersey received Steve Thomas, and the New York Islanders picked up Wendel Clark. Lemieux had won the Conn Smythe Trophy the season before as playoff MVP when New Jersey won the Stanley Cup. He became a key player for Colorado and helped win the Cup in 1995-96. He was then traded back to New Jersey with draft picks for forward Brian Rolston in November 1999.

9. Brian Rolston was then involved in another big trade as the Avs sent him to Boston with fellow forward Samuel Påhlsson, defender Martin Grenier, and a 1st round draft pick in March 2000 for blueliner Ray Bourque and forward Dave Andreychuk. Bourque helped Colorado win the Stanley Cup in 2000-01, but Andreychuk left after the season to sign with Buffalo.

10. Another Hall of Fame defenseman picked up by Colorado was Rob Blake from Los Angeles in February 2001. He

came with center Steve Reinprecht for winger Adam Deadmarsh, defender Aaron Miller, and two 1st round draft picks. Blake, who was soon scheduled to become an unrestricted free agent, was paired with Ray Bourque in the postseason. He notched 19 points in 23 games as the Avalanche won the Stanley Cup. Blake then played four more seasons with Colorado and posted 208 points in 322 games with 43 points in 68 playoff outings before re-signing with LA in 1996.

# CHAPTER 8:

# DRAFT DAY

## QUIZ TIME!

1. What season did the Avs draft Nathan MacKinnon 1st overall?

    a. 2011
    b. 2013
    c. 2014
    d. 2012

2. Who was the first player ever drafted by Colorado?

    a. John Tripp
    b. Tomi Kallio
    c. Brent Johnson
    d. Marc Denis

3. Quebec Nordiques player Mats Sundin became the first Swedish player to be drafted 1st overall in the NHL.

    a. True
    b. False

4. Which player did Colorado select 12th overall in 1998?

   a. Scott Parker

   b. Branko Radivojevič

   c. Alex Tanguay

   d. Martin Škoula

5. How many players did the Avalanche select in the 2000 Draft?

   a. 11

   b. 15

   c. 9

   d. 13

6. Colorado selected Tyson Barrie in which round of the 2009 Draft?

   a. 5th

   b. 3rd

   c. 1st

   d. 2nd

7. Which player drafted by Colorado has scored the most goals in the NHL as of 2019-20?

   a. Radim Vrbata

   b. Alex Tanguay

   c. Paul Stastny

   d. Matt Duchene

8. Colorado selected Matt Duchene 2nd overall in 2009.

   a. True

   b. False

9. How many top 10 picks did the Avs have between 2009 and 2019?

    a. 6

    b. 4

    c. 7

    d. 3

10. How many goaltenders have the Avs drafted as of 2019?

    a. 27

    b. 23

    c. 19

    d. 25

11. In 2012, Colorado selected only three players in the draft.

    a. True

    b. False

12. In the Avs' first 10 drafts, how many players selected in the $1^{st}$ round played fewer than 100 NHL games?

    a. 5

    b. 6

    c. 2

    d. 7

13. Who did Colorado select $21^{st}$ overall in 2004?

    a. Brad Richardson

    b. Brandon Yip

    c. Wojtek Wolski

    d. Paul Stastny

14. Michel Goulet was the first player drafted by the Nordiques.

    a. True
    b. False

15. How many defensemen has Colorado drafted as of 2019?

    a. 49
    b. 53
    c. 67
    d. 74

16. Which player was selected 63$^{rd}$ overall in 2001?

    a. Danny Bois
    b. Marek Svatoš
    c. Cody McCormick
    d. Peter Budaj

17. Colorado has drafted how many centers as of 2019?

    a. 66
    b. 52
    c. 36
    d. 42

18. Who did the Avs select 61$^{st}$ overall in 2002?

    a. Tom Gilbert
    b. Johnny Boychuk
    c. David Jones
    d. Jonas Johansson

19. Between 1988 and 1992, how many times did the Nordiques have the 1st overall draft pick?

    a. 1
    b. 4
    c. 2
    d. 3

20. Colorado selected Gabriel Landeskog 2nd overall in 2011.

    a. True
    b. False

# QUIZ ANSWERS

1. B – 2013

2. D – Marc Denis

3. A – True

4. C – Alex Tanguay

5. D – 13

6. B – 3rd

7. A – Radim Vrbata

8. B – False

9. C – 7

10. D – 25

11. B – False

12. A – 5

13. C – Wojtek Wolski

14. A – True

15. C – 67

16. D – Peter Budaj

17. B – 52

18. B – Johnny Boychuk

19. D – 3

20. A – True

# DID YOU KNOW?

1. Between 1999 and 2008, the Avs didn't fare too well in the draft. Their picks averaged just 117 games played in the NHL and 47 points, while the league average pick played 303 games and notched 165 points. Colorado's 1st round selections in this span averaged 165 points in 317 games, while the league average was 253 points in 508 games played. This meant the club's 1st rounders ranked 22nd in the league.

2. After the 2019 NHL Entry Draft was completed, the Quebec-Colorado franchise had drafted a total of 392 players since 1979. They were fortunate enough to draft 1st overall on four occasions, in 1989, 1990, 1991, and 2013. In addition, they had the 2nd overall pick in 2011.

3. The Nordiques owned the 1st overall pick from 1989 through 1991. Center Mats Sundin was taken in 1989 and posted 199 points in 324 regular-season games before being traded to Toronto in 1994. Winger Owen Nolan was chosen in 1989 and scored 216 points in 259 games before being traded to San Jose in 1995. Center Eric Lindros was picked in 1991 and traded to Philadelphia in 1992. Center Nathan MacKinnon was selected in 2013 by Colorado and had 495 points in 525 outings at the end of 2019-20.

4. The very first NHL Draft for the franchise was quite successful as five of the six players selected enjoyed fine

NHL careers. Those taken were winger Michel Goulet, center Dale Hunter, defenseman Lee Norwood, winger Anton Stastny, and blueliners Pierre Lacroix and Scott McGeown. Goulet was inducted into the Hockey Hall of Fame, and McGeown was the only one not to play in the NHL.

5. Michel Goulet was the first player drafted by the franchise as he was selected 20th overall in 1979 after playing the previous year in the WHA with the Birmingham Bulls. He played nearly 11 seasons in Quebec before being traded to Chicago in March 1990. The five-time All-Star played 1,089 regular-season NHL games with 548 goals and 1,153 points, and he holds the franchise record for 57 goals in a season, set in 1982-83.

6. Winger Anton Stastny was originally drafted by Philadelphia in 1978 with the 198th overall selection. The NHL nullified the pick, though, after ruling that Stastny was too young to be drafted. He re-entered the draft the next year and was taken by Quebec with the 84th pick. Stastny played his entire nine-season career with the team and tallied 252 goals and 636 points in 650 regular-season games, including eight straight campaigns with at least 25 goals.

7. The franchise's lowest-drafted player to carve out a decent NHL career was David Jones. The winger was selected in the 9th round with the 288th pick by Colorado in 2003, which was the fifth-to-the-last selection in the entire draft.

Jones played 462 regular-season NHL contests with 104 goals and 87 assists for 191 points. He played 272 games in Colorado before being traded to Calgary in 2013.

8. The highest-drafted goaltender by the franchise was Jocelyn Thibault, who went 10th overall to Quebec in 1993. He played 586 regular-season NHL contests with a record of 238-238-75, a .904 save percentage, a 2.75 goals-against average, and 39 shutouts. Thibault played just 47 games for Quebec and 10 for Colorado before being dealt to Montreal in 1995 in the famous Patrick Roy trade.

9. Tim Thomas was the lowest-drafted goalie by the organization to enjoy a fine NHL career. He was chosen with the 217th pick in 1994 but never played with Quebec-Colorado. Thomas signed as a free agent with Edmonton in 1998 and later with Boston. The two-time All-Star went on to win the Stanley Cup, the William M. Jennings Trophy, and two Vezina Trophies. He was also the oldest player to win the Conn Smythe Trophy at 37 and set an NHL record for most saves in a Stanley Cup Final with 238.

10. The first player drafted in Colorado was Marc Denis. The netminder was selected 25th overall in 1995. He played 28 games with the Avs from 1996-97 to 1999-2000 before being traded to Columbus in June 2000. Denis's NHL career consisted of 349 regular-season games. He led the league twice in losses and goals-against once. He also once led in games played, shots against, saves, and minutes.

# CHAPTER 9:

# GOALTENDER TIDBITS

## QUIZ TIME!

1. How many saves did Patrick Roy make with the Avalanche during his career?

    a. 12,540
    b. 11,924
    c. 11,897
    d. 12,165

2. Which goaltender lost 31 games in the 2016-17 regular season?

    a. Reto Berra
    b. Jeremy Smith
    c. Semyon Varlamov
    d. Calvin Pickard

3. Semyon Varlamov replaced Patrick Roy for most wins in a regular season with 41 in 2013-14.

    a. True
    b. False

4. How many regular-season wins did Peter Budaj have in 2006-07?

    a. 31

    b. 20

    c. 34

    d. 16

5. Which Avs goaltender faced 2,233 shots, the most in a single season?

    a. Semyon Varlamov

    b. Craig Anderson

    c. David Aebischer

    d. Peter Budaj

6. How many goaltenders did the Avs use in 2015-16?

    a. 3

    b. 5

    c. 4

    d. 6

7. What was Philipp Grubauer's save percentage in 2018-19?

    a. .915

    b. .916

    c. .920

    d. .917

8. Andrew Hammond played only 10 games with the Avalanche.

    a. True

    b. False

9. What is the highest save percentage recorded by an Avs goaltender in a single season?

    a. .928
    b. .925
    c. .927
    d. .929

10. Which goalie played 37 games and won 19 in 2017-18?

    a. Spencer Martin
    b. Calvin Pickard
    c. Jeremy Smith
    d. Jonathan Bernier

11. Goaltenders combined to make 2,082 saves in the 1999-2000 regular season.

    a. True
    b. False

12. What is the most shutouts a Colorado goaltender has recorded in a regular season?

    a. 8
    b. 10
    c. 9
    d. 7

13. What is the most games an Avs goalie has played in a regular season?

    a. 71
    b. 66
    c. 62
    d. 68

14. Patrick Roy had a career save percentage of .919.

    a. True
    b. False

15. How many games did Craig Anderson lose between 2009 and 2011?

    a. 42
    b. 56
    c. 50
    d. 39

16. Brian Elliot played a total of 12 games in 2010-11 and lost how many?

    a. 8
    b. 3
    c. 9
    d. 5

17. What was Jose Theodore's goals-against average in 2006-07?

    a. 2.81
    b. 3.47
    c. 2.44
    d. 3.26

18. What is the most saves made by a Colorado goaltender in a single season?

    a. 2,102
    b. 2,099
    c. 2,167
    d. 2,047

19. Jean-Sébastien Giguère started how many games for the Avs?

    a.  65

    b.  52

    c.  63

    d.  70

20. Jocelyn Thibault played only 10 games as a member of the Colorado Avalanche.

    a.  True

    b.  False

# QUIZ ANSWERS

1. B – 11,924

2. D – Calvin Pickard

3. A – True

4. A – 31

5. B – Craig Anderson

6. C – 4

7. D – .917

8. B – False

9. C – .927

10. D – Jonathan Bernier

11. A – True

12. C – 9

13. A – 71

14. B – False

15. C – 50

16. A – 8

17. D – 3.26

18. D – 2,047

19. C – 63

20. A – True

# DID YOU KNOW?

1. The Nordiques-Avalanche have used 52 different goaltenders since joining the NHL and just one of them, Patrick Roy, was inducted into the Hockey Hall of Fame. Four of the goalies played just one game for the team, and 14 of them played fewer than 10 contests.

2. Dan Bouchard played the most games in net while the club was based in Quebec, with 226 appearances between 1981 and 1985. He posted a winning record of 107-80-36 with a goals-against average of 3.59 and save percentage of .878. He led the league in games played and wins in 1978-79 while with the Atlanta Flames.

3. Although he made a name for himself with the Philadelphia Flyers, Ron Hextall played briefly with Quebec. He was acquired in the Eric Lindros trade in June 1992 and was then swapped to the New York Islanders a year later. While in Quebec, Hextall posted a 29-16-5 record in 54 games with a 3.35 goals-against average and a .888 save percentage and went 2-4 in the playoffs.

4. Ron Tugnutt was known for two things in Quebec, his unusual name and his amazing performance against the Boston Bruins on March 21, 1991. Tugnutt faced 73 shots in the game in Boston and made 70 saves to earn his team a 3-3 tie. The 70 saves were the second most in a regular-season game in NHL history.

5. Since moving to Colorado, the team has typically used two or three goaltenders per season. However, they used four in 2005-06, 2013-14, 2015-16, and 2017-18. The most the Avs have used in a season, though, has been five, which occurred in 2019-20. The goalies who played at least one game were Pavel Francouz, Philipp Grubauer, Antoine Bibeau, Michael Hutchinson, and Adam Werner.

6. One of the greatest seasons posted by a Colorado goalie was 2013-14 by Semyon Varlamov as he led the league and set a club record with 41 wins. He also faced the most shots in the NHL and made the most saves that year. Varlamov posted a 2.41 goals-against average and also set a club record save percentage in a season at .927. It was a great bounce-back campaign, considering he lost a league-high 21 games the year before in the 48-game shortened season.

7. The busiest season for a franchise goalie was endured by Craig Anderson in 2009-10. He played a club record 71 games and faced 2,233 shots while making 2,047 saves in 4,235 minutes played, all franchise highs. He posted a 38-25-7 record that campaign, with a goals-against average of 2.63, a .917 save percentage, and a league-high 186 goals against.

8. Just one of 23 goaltenders who played for Quebec managed to register a career goals-against average of under 3.00 with the team. Jocelyn Thibault just made it with a 2.95 average in 47 games. In addition, he's the only

goalie in Nordiques history to post a save percentage of at least .900 with the team as he registered a .901 percentage.

9.  Patrick Roy holds most of the franchise regular-season and playoff records for goaltending and was also the best playmaker in the crease. Roy earned an organization-high 17 assists with the Avalanche and was followed by Dan Bouchard (Quebec) with 11, Stéphane Fiset (Quebec and Colorado) with 9, Mario Gosselin (Quebec) with 8, and Peter Budaj (Colorado) with 7.

10. Peter Budaj is currently the third-longest serving goalie in franchise history with 242 games under his belt from 2005-06 to 2010-11. His record with the team was 135-101-91 with a 2.83 goals-against average and a .901 save percentage. Budaj left the Avs to sign as a free agent with Montreal in 2011.

# CHAPTER 10:

## ODDS & ENDS

### QUIZ TIME!

1. When Ray Bourque won the Stanley Cup with the Avs in 2000-01 he was in which NHL season?

    a. His 21st
    b. His 20th
    c. His 22nd
    d. His 19th

2. How many games did Colorado play at the McNichols Sports Arena before moving to the Pepsi Center?

    a. 174
    b. 186
    c. 162
    d. 170

3. In 2001, the Avs played and won their first international exhibition game in Stockholm, Sweden.

    a. True
    b. False

4. Which of the following players is NOT part of the "Triple Gold Club" (Stanley Cup, World Championship, and Olympic Gold Medal)?

   a. Joe Sakic
   b. Peter Forsberg
   c. Patrick Roy
   d. Valeri Kamensky

5. How many penalty minutes did the Avs total in the 2009-10 regular season?

   a. 1,043
   b. 1,001
   c. 988
   d. 1,104

6. How many hat tricks did Colorado score in its first season and postseason combined?

   a. 8
   b. 5
   c. 10
   d. 7

7. How many power-play goals did the Avs score in the 2000-01 regular season?

   a. 79
   b. 52
   c. 80
   d. 45

8. Patrick Roy would never skate on top of the red and blue lines on the ice due to superstition.

    a. True

    b. False

9. How many games did Colorado lose (including overtime losses) in 2016-17?

    a. 44

    b. 39

    c. 43

    d. 60

10. What was the first season the Avalanche didn't make the playoffs?

    a. 2008-09

    b. 2003-04

    c. 2006-07

    d. 2005-06

11. The Avs spent one season in the Pacific Division.

    a. True

    b. False

12. Colorado players scored on how many of their four penalty shot attempts in the 2005-06 season?

    a. 4

    b. 2

    c. 0

    d. 3

13. What team did the Avalanche face off against in the 2017 NHL Global Series?

    a. Ottawa Senators
    b. New Jersey Devils
    c. Edmonton Oilers
    d. Florida Panthers

14. The Avs have made the Conference Finals six times as of 2019.

    a. True
    b. False

15. When was Joe Sakic named general manager of the Avalanche?

    a. 2013
    b. 2015
    c. 2014
    d. 2016

16. What was the Avs' faceoff win percentage in the 2012-13 regular season?

    a. 50.4
    b. 52.7
    c. 49.5
    d. 51.1

17. How many even-strength goals did the Avs score in the 2007-08 regular season?

    a. 188
    b. 173

c. 164

d. 179

18. Colorado suffered how many overtime losses in 2014-15?

    a. 7

    b. 9

    c. 12

    d. 14

19. In the 2000-01 playoffs, how many of Colorado's games went into overtime?

    a. 5

    b. 2

    c. 4

    d. 6

20. The Avs scored 583 goals during their tenure at McNichols Sports Arena.

    a. True

    b. False

# QUIZ ANSWERS

1. C – His 22nd
2. D – 170
3. A – True
4. C – Patrick Roy
5. B – 1,001
6. A – 8
7. C – 80
8. A – True
9. D – 60
10. C – 2006-07
11. B – False
12. D – 3
13. A – Ottawa Senators
14. A – True
15. C – 2014
16. D – 51.1
17. B – 173
18. C – 12
19. D – 6
20. A – True

# DID YOU KNOW?

1. After the class of 2020 was announced, a total of 14 former Nordiques and Avalanche players have made it to the Hockey Hall of Fame. Those who played for Quebec only are forwards Michel Goulet, Guy Lafleur, Peter Stastny, and Mats Sundin. Those who played for Quebec and Colorado are centers Peter Forsberg and Joe Sakic. Those who played with Colorado only are goaltender Patrick Roy, defenders Ray Bourque and Rob Blake, and forwards Jarome Iginla, Paul Kariya, Jari Kurri, Dave Andreychuk, and Teemu Selanne.

2. Bryan Trottier won a Stanley Cup with Colorado in 2001 and is in the Hall of Fame as a player. In addition, Guy Lapointe was once an assistant coach with the Nordiques and is also in the Hall of Fame as a player. Hall of Fame goaltender Jacques Plante was once coach and general manager of the Nordiques but only when the team competed in the WHA.

3. Nine players have been named to the NHL's All-Rookie Team since 1984. They are defender Bruce Bell (1984-85) and forward Peter Forsberg (1994-95) for Quebec, while the rest played for the Avalanche. They are forwards Chris Drury and Milan Hejduk (1998-99), defender John Michael Liles (2003-04), Paul Stastny (2006-07), Matt Duchene (2009-10), Gabriel Landeskog (2011-12), and Nathan MacKinnon (2012-13).

4. As of 2019, a total of 10 franchise players had been named to the NHL's end-of-season First or Second All-Star Teams at least once. Those honored for their play are goaltenders Semyon Varlamov and Patrick Roy; defenders Sandis Ozoliņš, Ray Bourque, and Rob Blake; and forwards Peter Forsberg, Milan Hejduk, Nathan MacKinnon, and Joe Sakic. Winger Michel Goulet was the only Quebec player to make the teams, and he leads the way with five selections.

5. The Nordiques had 10 different head coaches when they played in the NHL. The first was Jacques Demers, followed by Maurice Filion, Michel Bergeron, Andre Savard, Ron Lapointe, Jean Perron, Michel Bergeron again, Dave Chambers, Pierre Page, and Marc Crawford. Bergeron coached from 1980 to 1987 and again in 1989-90.

6. Since moving to Colorado, the club's head coaches have been: Marc Crawford, Bob Hartley, Tony Granato, Joel Quenneville, Tony Granato again, Joe Sacco, Patrick Roy, and Jared Bednar. Crawford and Hartley led the team to Stanley Cup championships, while Granato coached from 2002 to 2004 and again in 2008 and 2009.

7. Michel Bergeron was the longest-serving coach in franchise history as he posted a record of 265-283-86 in 634 regular-season contests with the Nordiques. He also went 31-37 in 68 playoff outings. Maurice Filion was the shortest-reigning coach as he was behind the bench for just six games in 1980 with a record of 1-3-2. Bob Hartley coached the most postseason games at 80, with a record of 49-31.

8. As for general managers, Maurice Filion was in charge of the club from May 1974 to April 1988, which means he was with the club in the WHA and when it merged into the NHL in 1979. He then returned to the fold as interim general manager from February 2 to May 5, 1990.

9. When Filion left the GM post after his first stint, he was followed by Martin Madden and Pierre Page in Quebec. Pierre Lacroix took over in Quebec on May 24, 1994, and was with the club when it moved to Colorado. Lacroix held the job for exactly 12 years as he left the job on May 24, 1996. He was then followed by François Giguère, Greg Sherman, and current GM Joe Sakic, who took the job on September 19, 2014.

10. Pierre Lacroix was the most successful general manager in franchise history as he won two Stanley Cups, two Presidents' Trophies, two conference titles, and nine division titles and made the playoffs in 11 of his 12 seasons. Lacroix acquired his son Eric Lacroix from Los Angeles in a 1996 trade and then dealt him back to LA two years later.

# CHAPTER 11:

# AVALANCHE ON THE BLUE LINE

## QUIZ TIME!

1. What was Sandis Ozolinš's highest point total with Colorado?

    a. 54
    b. 68
    c. 52
    d. 64

2. How many points did Rob Blake score in the 2000-01 playoffs?

    a. 17
    b. 20
    c. 22
    d. 19

3. Adam Foote played 967 regular-season games with the Avalanche.

    a. True
    b. False

4. This Avs defenseman played all 82 games in 2002-03?

   a. Greg de Vries
   b. Martin Škoula
   c. Rob Blake
   d. Derek Morris

5. Who led Colorado in hits with 228 during the 2018-19 season?

   a. Tyson Barrie
   b. Ian Cole
   c. Nikita Zadorov
   d. Patrick Nemeth

6. What was Zach Redmond's team-leading plus/minus in 2015-16?

   a. +43
   b. +25
   c. +16
   d. +5

7. How many Avs defenders had a plus/minus of at least +10 in 1998-99?

   a. 1
   b. 3
   c. 2
   d. 4

8. Ten blueliners played at least 10 games in the 2003-04 season.

   a. True
   b. False

9. John-Michael Liles scored how many power-play goals in 2006-07?

    a. 3
    b. 8
    c. 10
    d. 6

10. Which defenseman had 12 assists and a team-high +27 in the 2017-18 season?

    a. Andrei Mironov
    b. David Warsofsky
    c. Anton Lindholm
    d. Patrick Nemeth

11. Tyson Barrie scored at least 12 goals three seasons in a row.

    a. True
    b. False

12. Which defenseman blocked 143 shots and registered 107 hits in 2008-09?

    a. Jordan Leopold
    b. Scott Hannan
    c. Ruslan Salei
    d. Brett Clark

13. How many defenders suited up in the Avs' regular season in 2010-11?

    a. 20
    b. 13

c.  17

d.  9

14. Fedor Tyutin had the lowest plus/minus of any blueliner on the team in 2016-17 at -34.

    a.  True

    b.  False

15. How many shots on net did Kyle Quincy attempt in 2009-10?

    a.  360

    b.  154

    c.  269

    d.  311

16. Which defenseman scored 51 points and totaled 94 penalty minutes in 2005-06?

    a.  Kārlis Skrastiņš

    b.  John-Michael Liles

    c.  Patrice Brisebois

    d.  Rob Blake

17. This defenseman blocked 256 shots in 2015-16.

    a.  François Beauchemin

    b.  Erik Johnson

    c.  Nick Holden

    d.  Tyson Barrie

18. Ray Bourque led all Avalanche defensemen with how many assists in 2000-01?

a. 50

b. 49

c. 52

d. 62

19. How many penalty minutes did Adam Foote record in 1996-97?

    a. 140

    b. 135

    c. 116

    d. 154

20. Derek Morris earned 40 assists in 2002-03.

    a. True

    b. False

# QUIZ ANSWERS

1. B – 68

2. D – 19

3. B – False

4. A – Greg de Vries

5. C – Nikita Zadorov

6. D – +5

7. D – 4

8. A – True

9. B – 8

10. D – Patrick Nemeth

11. A – True

12. C – Ruslan Salei

13. C – 17

14. B – False

15. D – 311

16. D – Rob Blake

17. A – François Beauchemin

18. C – 52

19. B – 135

20. B – False

# DID YOU KNOW?

1. The highest-scoring defenseman in franchise history is Tyson Barrie. He notched 75 goals and 307 points in 484 games between 2012 and 2019, with 14 points in 21 playoff games. He was traded to Toronto in July 2019 with a year remaining on his contract. The Avalanche assumed he'd be seeking a multi-million dollar, long-term deal as an unrestricted free agent and felt confident enough in their high-scoring blue line prospects to deal him.

2. One of the reasons the Avs traded Tyson Barrie was the emergence of promising young defenseman Cale Makar. He was selected 4th overall in the 2017 Draft and broke into the NHL as a rookie in 2019-20. Makar didn't disappoint, as he racked up 12 goals, 28 assists, and 50 points with a +12 rating in 57 games. This makes Makar the highest-scoring rookie defender in franchise history.

3. Before Cale Makar became the highest-scoring blueliner in club history, he actually starred in the previous season's playoffs. He played in the 2018-19 postseason and tallied six points in 10 games. He scored his first NHL goal on his first shot on net against Calgary in the playoffs a day after signing an entry-level contract. This made Makar the first blueliner in NHL history to score a postseason goal in his league debut.

4. John-Michael Liles was an offensive blueliner who skated

with the Avalanche from 2003 to 2011. Liles played 523 games with the Avs and chipped in with 68 goals and 275 points. He led all rookie defenders in scoring in 2003-04 and made the NHL All-Rookie Team as the highest-scoring rookie rearguard in Avalanche history and second-highest in franchise history at the time.

5. The highest-scoring rookie defender for Quebec was Bruce Bell in 1984-85. He was drafted 52nd overall in 1983 and posted six goals and 37 points in his first NHL season. Surprisingly, he was traded to St. Louis in October 1985 for fellow defender Gilbert Delorme.

6. Adam Foote was drafted 22nd overall by Quebec in 1989 and won two Stanley Cups with Colorado. The blueliner left the team and signed as a free agent with Columbus in 2005. He returned to Colorado in a 2008 trade and finished his career there, acting as captain from 2009 to 2011. Foote retired in 2011 and had his jersey retired by the franchise. He was the last Nordiques player to skate in the NHL.

7. Another solid defender for the organization was Sandis Ozoliņš, who was acquired in a 1995 trade for winger Owen Nolan. He helped the team win the Stanley Cup in his first season with 19 points in 22 playoff games. Ozoliņš then posted 23 goals and 68 points for the Avs in 1996-97 and was named to the NHL's First All-Star Team.

8. One of the most aggressive blueliners was Randy Moller, who was drafted 11th overall by Quebec in 1981. He broke into the league as a 19-year-old rookie and played with the

team until being traded in 1989. Moller served 1,002 penalty minutes for Quebec in 508 games with 140 minutes in 48 playoff encounters. He would go on to receive 1,692 minutes in 815 career games.

9. When it comes to defensive rearguards, Sylvain Lefebvre was one of the best after being acquired by Quebec from Toronto in the 1994 trade that saw Mats Sundin leave town. Lefebvre helped the Avs win the Stanley Cup in 1995-96 and would play 368 regular-season and playoff games with the franchise. He contributed 65 points in those contests with a +68 rating.

10. The Avalanche decided to take a gamble on Todd Gill in 2001 and signed him as a free agent. Gill had twice led Toronto defensemen in scoring during his career and was a former captain of the San Jose Sharks. He posted just four assists in 36 games with Colorado, though, before they released him just seven months after signing him. Gill soon retired with 354 points in 1,007 regular-season NHL games.

# CHAPTER 12:

# CENTERS OF ATTENTION

## QUIZ TIME!

1. Nathan MacKinnon led the Avs in goals and points in 2018-19. How many goals did he score?

    a. 52

    b. 39

    c. 46

    d. 41

2. Joe Sakic holds the Avs' record for most points in a season with how many?

    a. 118

    b. 132

    c. 120

    d. 125

3. Peter Forsberg had the most points for Colorado in the 2001-02 playoffs with 27.

    a. True

    b. False

4. Which center had 116 penalty minutes in 2005-06?

    a. Brett McLean
    b. Ian Laperrière
    c. Dan Hinote
    d. Pierre Turgeon

5. Who had a plus/minus of -10 in 1997-98?

    a. Jari Kurri
    b. Tom Fitzgerald
    c. Mike Ricci
    d. Stéphane Yelle

6. How many centers suited up for Colorado in the 2017-18 season?

    a. 8
    b. 10
    c. 7
    d. 9

7. Matt Duchene had a faceoff win percentage of what in the 2015-16 season?

    a. 52.4
    b. 55.3
    c. 57.9
    d. 54.8

8. Paul Stastny scored 10 game-winning goals in 2009-10.

    a. True
    b. False

9. Which player delivered 72 hits, the most of any center during the 2011-12 season?

   a. Daniel Winnik
   b. Jay McClement
   c. Ryan O'Reilly
   d. Paul Stastny

10. Colorado centers combined for how many points in the 2013-14 playoffs?

    a. 17
    b. 20
    c. 13
    d. 29

11. Jari Kurri played center for Colorado.

    a. True
    b. False

12. How many assists did Ryan O'Reilly tally in 2011-12?

    a. 37
    b. 13
    c. 36
    d. 14

13. Which center recorded 22 penalty minutes in his 11 games played in 1997-98?

    a. Dale Hunter
    b. Josef Marha
    c. Tom Fitzgerald
    d. Serge Aubin

14. Carl Söderberg took 190 shots on goal in 2018-19.

    a. True
    b. False

15. Alexander Kerfoot scored how many points as a rookie with Colorado?

    a. 42
    b. 38
    c. 43
    d. 36

16. What was the lowest plus/minus for an Avs center in 2013-14?

    a. -31
    b. -16
    c. -23
    d. -11

17. How many points did Tyler Arnason post in his Colorado career?

    a. 35
    b. 40
    c. 102
    d. 133

18. Who scored 19 goals in 67 games in the 2001-02 season?

    a. Dan Hinote
    b. Stéphane Yelle
    c. Steve Reinprecht
    d. Steve Moore

19. Who was the only center to play all 82 games in 2013-14?

    a.  Nathan MacKinnon
    b.  Ryan O'Reilly
    c.  Matt Duchene
    d.  Marc-André Cliche

20. Joe Sakic played only 30 games in his final season in Colorado.

    a.  True
    b.  False

# QUIZ ANSWERS

1. D – 41

2. C – 120

3. A – True

4. B – Ian Laperrière

5. D – Stéphane Yelle

6. A – 8

7. C – 57.9

8. B – False

9. B – Jay McClement

10. D – 29

11. B – False

12. A – 37

13. C – Tom Fitzgerald

14. B – False

15. C – 43

16. D – -11

17. B – 40

18. C – Steve Reinprecht

19. A – Nathan MacKinnon

20. B – False

# DID YOU KNOW?

1. There are four former Nordiques-Avalanche centers in the Hockey Hall of Fame. These are: Peter Forsberg, Joe Sakic, Peter Stastny, and Mats Sundin. Stastny and Sundin played only for Quebec, while Forsberg and Sakic played for both Quebec and Colorado.

2. Peter Forsberg arrived in Quebec in 1992 from Philadelphia in the Eric Lindros deal. He played 591 games with 217 goals, 755 points, and a +210 rating, and added 58 goals and 159 points in 140 playoff games. The three-time All-Star won two Stanley Cups with the franchise along with the Calder, Art Ross, and Hart Trophies. Forsberg signed as a free agent with Philadelphia in 2005 and returned to Colorado as a free agent in 2008.

3. The franchise's second leading scorer is Peter Stastny, who joined Quebec in 1980 as a free agent with his brother Anton after defecting from Czechoslovakia. Stastny was the NHL's rookie of the year in 1980-81 with 109 points. He registered 380 goals and 1,048 points with Quebec in 737 games and had 24 goals and 81 points in 64 playoff outings. Stastny was then traded to New Jersey in 1990 for defenders Craig Wolanin and Randy Velischek.

4. Peter Stastny's son, Paul Stastny, also played with the franchise after being drafted 55th overall in 2005. The center tallied 160 goals and 458 points in 538 contests, adding 18

points in 22 playoff games. Stastny left Colorado in 2014 when he signed with St. Louis as a free agent. He played with the Vegas Golden Knights in 2019-20.

5. The most robust center in franchise history was Dale Hunter, who was assessed a club-record 1,562 penalty minutes in 535 games with Quebec and Colorado. He also notched 142 goals and 464 points. Hunter racked up another 359 penalty minutes in 86 playoff games while tallying 46 points. He started his NHL career in Quebec in 1980, was traded to Washington in 1987, and traded to Colorado in March 1999. He then retired at the end of the season.

6. Not too far behind Dale Hunter on the all-time penalty list is Paul Gillis, who ranks fourth in franchise history with 1,354 minutes. Gillis played 576 games with Quebec from 1982-83 until he was traded to Chicago in March 1991. He scored 233 points in 576 games with the team and added 16 points in 35 playoff matches, where he served another 154 penalty minutes.

7. Nathan MacKinnon has lived up to his billing after being drafted 1st overall by Colorado in 2013. By the end of the 2019-20 regular season, he had 190 goals and 495 points in 525 outings, with 29 points in 25 playoff games. This includes 115 goals and 289 points in 225 matches in his last three seasons. The 2013-14 rookie of the year led the league with 12 game-winning goals in 2017-18 and in shots on net the following two seasons.

8.  Ryan O'Reilly is known for winning the Conn Smythe Trophy in 2019, when he led St. Louis to the Stanley Cup. However, he started his career on October 1, 2009, as the youngest player in Colorado history to skate in a regular-season NHL game. He then became the first Avs player to score two shorthanded goals in a game, led the NHL in takeaways two seasons in a row, and won the Lady Byng Trophy for 2013-14. O'Reilly was traded to Buffalo in 2015.

9.  Although Pierre Turgeon played just 79 regular-season games for the Avalanche at the end of his career, he was one of the best free-agent signings the club made in 2005. He made a considerable impact in his short stint by adding depth and scoring 20 goals and 53 points while averaging just 12:13 minutes per game. Turgeon then retired in 2007 at the age of 37 after scoring 515 goals and 1,327 points in 1,294 career regular-season games.

10. Matt Duchene was drafted 3rd overall by Colorado in 2009 and tallied 178 goals and 428 points in 586 regular-season outings. He played just eight postseason games, though, and requested a trade. During a November 2017 game, he was sent to Ottawa in a three-team deal that included Nashville. The Avs acquired plenty in return in Samuel Girard, Vladislav Kamenev, and a 2nd round draft pick from Nashville, as well as Shane Bowers, Andrew Hammond, and 1st and 3rd round picks from Ottawa.

# CHAPTER 13:

# THE WINGERS TAKE FLIGHT

## QUIZ TIME!

1. Which winger scored 39 goals in the Avs' inaugural season?

    a. Valeri Kamensky

    b. Claude Lemieux

    c. Chris Simon

    d. Scott Young

2. Who had 63 penalty minutes in 81 games during the 1996-97 season?

    a. Brent Severyn

    b. Keith Jones

    c. Adam Deadmarsh

    d. Mike Keane

3. Milan Hejduk scored 14 power-play goals in 2005-06.

    a. True

    b. False

4. Which player had 53 points in 2015-16?

    a. Mikkel Bødker

    b. Blake Comeau

    c. Gabriel Landeskog

    d. Jarome Iginla

5. Who led the Avs in goals with 28 in 2009-10?

    a. Milan Hejduk

    b. Chris Stewart

    c. T.J. Galiardi

    d. David Jones

6. What was Mikko Rantanen's plus/minus in 2016-17?

    a. -25

    b. +13

    c. +7

    d. -9

7. How many points did Jarome Iginla score in his first season in Colorado?

    a. 61

    b. 47

    c. 27

    d. 59

8. The Avs had 11 wingers play at least one game in 2018-19.

    a. True

    b. False

9. How many power-play goals did Andrew Brunette score in the 2007-08 playoffs?

    a. 0
    b. 5
    c. 3
    d. 6

10. Avalanche wingers combined for how many game-winning goals in 2016-17?

    a. 13
    b. 10
    c. 7
    d. 9

11. Matt Calvert had the most hits of any winger in 2018-19.

    a. True
    b. False

12. How many points did Alex Tanguay score in 2000-01?

    a. 77
    b. 48
    c. 67
    d. 51

13. Which winger led Colorado in hits in 2013-14 with 178?

    a. Gabriel Landeskog
    b. Jamie McGinn
    c. Patrick Bordeleau
    d. P.A. Parenteau

14. Eric Lacroix earned 38 assists in 1997-98.

   a. True
   b. False

15. Who was the only Avs winger to score a shorthanded goal in 1999-2000?

   a. Shjon Podein
   b. Milan Hejduk
   c. Jeff Odgers
   d. Adam Deadmarsh

16. How many goals did Avs wingers score on penalty shots in the 2005-06 regular season?

   a. 4
   b. 1
   c. 2
   d. 5

17. How man career regular-season points did Valeri Kamensky notch with the Avalanche?

   a. 153
   b. 146
   c. 270
   d. 261

18. Who had 259 penalty minutes in 1998-99, the most in an Avalanche season?

   a. Chris Simon
   b. Jeff Odgers
   c. Scott Parker
   d. Claude Lemieux

19. Which winger scored 26 goals in 62 games during the 2007-08 campaign?

    a. Ryan Smith
    b. Wojtek Wolski
    c. Andrew Brunette
    d. Marek Svatoš

20. Blake Comeau had at least 50 penalty minutes in each of his three seasons with the Avs.

    a. True
    b. False

# QUIZ ANSWERS

1.  B – Claude Lemieux

2.  D – Mike Keane

3.  A – True

4.  C – Gabriel Landeskog

5.  B – Chris Stewart

6.  A – -25

7.  D – 59

8.  A – True

9.  C – 3

10. D – 9

11. B – False

12. A – 77

13. C – Patrick Bordeleau

14. B – False

15. A – Shjon Podein

16. C – 2

17. D – 261

18. B – Jeff Odgers

19. D – Marek Svatoš

20. A – True

# DID YOU KNOW?

1. The seven former Nordiques-Avalanche wingers who made it into the Hockey Hall of Fame in Toronto are Michel Goulet, Guy Lafleur, Teemu Selanne, Paul Kariya, Dave Andreychuk, Jari Kurri, and Jarome Iginla. Goulet and Lafleur played for Quebec only, while the rest of the wingers played for Colorado.

2. Jarome Iginla is the latest winger to make the Hall of Fame in 2020. He signed with Colorado in 2014 and tallied 124 points in 225 regular-season games, leading the team in goals with 29 in his first season. He retired with 625 goals and 1,300 points in 1,554 regular-season outings. Iginla was a four-time All-Star, a member of the All-Rookie Team, and winner of the Rocket Richard Trophy (twice), Lester B. Pearson Award, Art Ross Trophy, King Clancy Memorial Award, NHL Foundation Player Award, and the Mark Messier Leadership Award.

3. Colorado tried to strengthen its squad by signing wingers Teemu Selanne and Paul Kariya as free agents in 2003, but things didn't work out too well. The pair cost just $7 million for a season as they both took huge pay cuts. However, the Hall-of-Famers combined for just 27 goals and 68 points in 129 regular-season games, and the Avs were knocked out of the playoffs in the second round.

4. The acquisition of Jari Kurri and Dave Andreychuk was

also somewhat disappointing. Kurri signed as a 37-year-old free agent in 1997, notched five goals and 22 points in 74 regular and postseason games, and then promptly retired. Andreychuk posted four goals and eight points in 31 combined games after being acquired in the 2000 trade that brought Ray Bourque from Boston. He then signed as a free agent with Buffalo several weeks later.

5. Guy Lafleur's stint with Quebec was slightly better than some of the other Hall of Fame wingers but wasn't spectacular. He spent the last two years of his career there after signing as a 38-year-old free agent in 1989. He posted 68 points in 92 games over two seasons, and the team didn't make the playoffs. Lafleur was traded to Minnesota in May 1991 and hung up his skates.

6. Since Guy Lafleur was close to the age of 40 and at the end of his career, his time in Quebec may not appear that bad. However, there's a side note to the story. When Quebec signed the free agent, they had to give up a 5th round draft choice in 1990 as compensation to the New York Rangers. That pick was used to select Hall of Fame defenseman Sergei Zubov, who went on to win two Stanley Cups and post 771 points in 1,068 regular-season contests.

7. One free-agent signing that did work out well was winger Andrew Brunette. He inked a deal with Colorado in 2005 and played three full seasons without missing a game. Brunette contributed 70 goals and 205 points in 246 games, with 27 power-play goals and six game-winners. He also

added 17 points in 19 playoff games before signing with Minnesota in 2008.

8.  Milan Hejduk was a success story after being drafted by Quebec in 1994. The winger played his entire career with the Avs from 1998 to 2013, with 375 goals and 805 points in 1,020 games. He added 34 goals and 76 points in 112 playoff games and helped the team win the Stanley Cup with 23 points in 23 games in the 2000-01 postseason. Hejduk led the NHL in goals in 2002-03, with 50, as well as leading in even-strength goals, goals per game, and shooting percentage.

9.  Winger Alex Tanguay also contributed greatly to Colorado's success as he tallied 21 points in 23 playoff outings to help hoist the 2001 Stanley Cup. He played from 1999 to 2006 and was then traded to Calgary. The Avs reacquired him seven years later from the Flames, and Tanguay played in Denver before being traded again in February 2016. He led the NHL in shooting percentage twice with Colorado. He scored 488 points in 598 games and added 50 points in 83 playoff matches.

10. After being drafted 10th overall by Colorado in 2015, Mikko Rantanen has blossomed into one of the NHL's top wingers. By the end of the 2019-20 regular season, he had racked up 99 goals and 250 points in 281 games with 18 points in 18 playoff games. This included 212 points in 197 games over his last three seasons.

# CHAPTER 14:

# THE HEATED RIVALRIES

## QUIZ TIME!

1. How many fights broke out in the game between Colorado and Detroit on March 26, 1997?

    a. 7

    b. 6

    c. 9

    d. 4

2. Which team did the Avalanche beat 12-2 on December 5, 1995?

    a. Dallas Stars

    b. Boston Bruins

    c. Edmonton Oilers

    d. San Jose Sharks

3. Patrick Roy and fellow goaltender Mike Vernon of Detroit fought during the "Brawl in Hockeytown" in March 1997.

    a. True

    b. False

4. Who did Colorado beat in the Finals to win their second Stanley Cup in 2000-01?

    a. Ottawa Senators
    b. Florida Panthers
    c. New Jersey Devils
    d. Detroit Red Wings

5. The Avs have won how many of their 166 regular-season games against the Edmonton Oilers?

    a. 90
    b. 78
    c. 66
    d. 103

6. How many goals did Colorado score against Vancouver in the 2000-01 regular season?

    a. 21
    b. 30
    c. 16
    d. 24

7. In 1996-97, the Avs took how many points out of a possible eight against Columbus?

    a. 6
    b. 3
    c. 5
    d. 8

8. The Avalanche lost their first-ever meeting against the Vegas Golden Knights 7-0 in 2017.

a. True

b. False

9. Which team did Colorado lose to in the 2020 Stadium Series game?

a. Detroit Red Wings

b. Los Angeles Kings

c. Anaheim Ducks

d. Philadelphia Flyers

10. The Avs lost how many games against Vancouver in the 2011-12 season?

a. 4

b. 3

c. 6

d. 2

11. The Avalanche has NEVER played the Toronto Maple Leafs in the playoffs.

a. True

b. False

12. How many goals did Colorado score against Edmonton in the 2006-07 campaign?

a. 25

b. 27

c. 32

d. 41

13. As of 2019, how many regular-season and playoff games have the Avs lost to the Calgary Flames?

a. 80

b. 75

c. 63

d. 72

14. Colorado scored 15 goals against the Florida Panthers in the 1995-96 Stanley Cup Finals.

    a. True

    b. False

15. Which team eliminated the Avs from the Conference Finals in 1998-99?

    a. Dallas Stars

    b. San Jose Sharks

    c. Los Angeles Kings

    d. St. Louis Blues

16. How many times did Colorado and Detroit meet in the postseason from 1995 to 2002?

    a. 3

    b. 4

    c. 5

    d. 6

17. Through 143 regular-season matchups against the Chicago Blackhawks, how many games has Colorado won?

    a. 64

    b. 78

    c. 55

    d. 71

18. How many goals did Colorado tally against the Winnipeg Jets in the 2018-19 season?

   a. 22
   b. 18
   c. 33
   d. 20

19. The Avalanche has scored how many goals against the Buffalo Sabres in 147 regular-season games?

   a. 507
   b. 484
   c. 487
   d. 523

20. Colorado went unbeaten against seven teams in the 2013-14 season.

   a. True
   b. False

# QUIZ ANSWERS

1. C – 9

2. D – San Jose Sharks

3. A – True

4. C – New Jersey Devils

5. B – 78

6. A – 21

7. D – 8

8. A – True

9. B – Los Angeles Kings

10. C – 6

11. A – True

12. C – 32

13. B – 75

14. A – True

15. A – Dallas Stars

16. C – 5

17. D – 71

18. D – 20

19. A – 507

20. B – False

# DID YOU KNOW?

1. When the Quebec-Colorado franchise entered the NHL in the 1979 merger, it did so with three other former WHA clubs. Therefore, there were already existing rivalries with these teams, the Winnipeg Jets, Edmonton Oilers, and the New England Whalers, who would become the Hartford Whalers and then the Carolina Hurricanes.

2. The biggest NHL rivals for the Quebec Nordiques were the Montreal Canadiens, who also played in the province of Quebec and were located just 156 miles down the highway. The rivalry was known as "The Battle of Quebec," and the teams met five times in the playoffs, with Montreal winning three of the series. One infamous 1984 playoff brawl was known as "The Good Friday Massacre" and resulted in 252 penalty minutes and 11 player ejections.

3. The Quebec vs. Montreal rivalry also extended to politics as the franchises became symbols for opposing political parties. In addition, beer distribution fueled the flames because the Nordiques were owned by the Carling O'Keefe brewery, and the Canadiens were owned by the rival Molson brewing company. The two organizations clashed frequently over television rights as well, but once Quebec relocated to Colorado, the rivalry vanished.

4. Once settled in Colorado, a huge rivalry developed with

the Detroit Red Wings. The teams met in the 1996 Western Conference Finals, with the Avs winning in six games. During the final game, Colorado winger Claude Lemieux checked Kris Draper from behind and planted him face-first into the boards, which resulted in Draper needing facial reconstructive surgery. In March 1997, "the Brawl in Hockeytown" took place in Detroit, featuring nine fights and 148 penalty minutes.

5. Another brawl between Colorado and Detroit took place in May 1997 in Game 4 of the Western Conference Finals in Detroit. Colorado coach Marc Crawford and Detroit coach Scotty Bowman screamed obscenities at each other in the fight-filled game, with Bowman stating, "I knew your father before you did, and I don't think he'd be very proud of how you're acting." Detroit won 6-0, and the NHL fined Crawford $10,000 for his actions.

6. On November 11, 1997, Detroit's Darren McCarty and Claude Lemieux fought each other just after the game's opening faceoff. On April 1, 1998, the squads engaged in yet another brawl in Detroit. Goaltenders Patrick Roy and Chris Osgood fought at center ice and both were ejected from the game, which featured 228 penalty minutes. There was also a brawl in Colorado on March 23, 2002, when Patrick Roy's attempt to fight fellow goaltender Dominik Hašek was thwarted by the officials.

7. The Colorado vs. Detroit rivalry was quite evident between 1996 and 2002, as the teams played each other

five times in seven playoff seasons. Colorado won the series in 1995-96, 1998-99, and 1999-2000, while Detroit won in 1996-97 and 2001-02. In addition, the two clubs combined for five Stanley Cups in those seven years with the Avs winning it in 1995-96 and 2000-01. The teams didn't meet in the playoffs again until 2007-08.

8. At the conclusion of the 2018-19 postseason, the Quebec-Colorado franchise had played a total of 48 playoff series with a record of 26-22. They had met a total of 22 different teams with a winning record against nine of them, a losing record against eight, and an even record against the other five. Of the 22 opponents, the Nordiques-Avalanche franchise has played just one series against nine of them.

9. The teams the franchise has met the most in the playoffs are the Detroit Red Wings (6), Montreal Canadiens (5), and San Jose Sharks (5). Their playoff series record against Detroit is 3-3, while it's 2-3 against both Montreal and San Jose.

10. The team the franchise has had the most success against since joining the NHL to the conclusion of the 2019-20 season is the Columbus Blue Jackets. They've never met in the playoffs, but the Avalanche has a 40-20-1 record for a 66.4 winning percentage. The team that gives the club the most trouble is the Washington Capitals as their combined record is 33-45-9 for a 43.1 winning percentage. The franchise has never met Washington in the playoffs, either.

# CHAPTER 15:

# THE AWARDS SECTION

## QUIZ TIME!

1. Which Avs player won the Calder Memorial Trophy in 1998-99?

    a. Milan Hejduk

    b. Chris Drury

    c. Adam Deadmarsh

    d. Scott Parker

2. How many major NHL awards did Joe Sakic win in 2000-01?

    a. 2

    b. 3

    c. 1

    d. 4

3. Colorado won the Presidents' Trophy in its inaugural season.

    a. True

    b. False

4. From 1995 to 2014, how many division titles did Colorado win?

    a. 6

    b. 10

    c. 9

    d. 5

5. Peter Forsberg and Milan Hejduk shared the NHL Plus-Minus Award in 2002-03 with what plus/minus?

    a. +48

    b. +55

    c. +64

    d. +52

6. How many points did Nathan MacKinnon tally when he won the Calder Memorial Trophy in 2013-14?

    a. 63

    b. 59

    c. 60

    d. 72

7. Colorado has won the Clarence S. Campbell Bowl how many times as of 2019?

    a. 3

    b. 4

    c. 2

    d. 5

8. Patrick Roy won the Conn Smythe Trophy in the 1995-96 playoffs.

a. True

b. False

9. How many Colorado players participated in the 2012 NHL All-Star Skills Competition?

   a. 4

   b. 1

   c. 2

   d. 3

10. Which Avs player won the Lady Byng Memorial Trophy in 2013-14?

    a. Erik Johnson

    b. Matt Duchene

    c. Ryan O'Reilly

    d. Paul Stastny

11. Colorado won eight division titles in a row from 1995 to 2003.

    a. True

    b. False

12. How many team and player awards did Colorado win from 1995-96 to 2013-14?

    a. 28

    b. 20

    c. 18

    d. 24

13. Who was the first Avs defenseman named to the NHL All-Rookie Team?

a. Derek Morris

b. Ossi Väänänen

c. John-Michael Liles

d. Martin Škoula

14. Peter Forsberg won the Viking Award for best Swedish player three times.

a. True

b. False

15. What season did Patrick Roy win the William M. Jennings Trophy?

a. 1995-96

b. 2001-02

c. 2002-03

d. 1997-98

16. Who was the first Avalanche player inducted into the Hockey Hall of Fame?

a. Patrick Roy

b. Joe Sakic

c. Ray Bourque

d. Jari Kurri

17. Who won the King Clancy Memorial Trophy in 2000-01?

a. Rob Blake

b. Adam Foote

c. Shjon Podein

d. Ray Bourque

18.

19. How many Avs played in the 2001 All-Star Game?

    a. 4

    b. 3

    c. 5

    d. 6

20. Who was the first coach to win the Jack Adams Awards for Colorado?

    a. Marc Crawford

    b. Joel Quenneville

    c. Patrick Roy

    d. Bob Hartley

21. Semyon Varlamov won the Vezina Trophy in 2014-15.

    a. True

    b. False

# QUIZ ANSWERS

1. B – Chris Drury

2. D – 4

3. A – True

4. C – 9

5. D – +52

6. A – 63

7. C – 2

8. B – False

9. B – 1

10. C – Ryan O'Reilly

11. A – True

12. D – 24

13. C – John-Michael Liles

14. A – True

15. B – 2001-02

16. D – Jari Kurri

17. C – Shjon Podein

18. C – 5

19. C – Patrick Roy

20. B – False

# DID YOU KNOW?

1. The Nordiques-Avalanche franchise has won numerous individual and team awards since entering the NHL. These include: Stanley Cup (2), Clarence S. Campbell Bowl (2), Presidents' Trophy (2), Art Ross Trophy (1), Calder Memorial Trophy (5), Conn Smythe Trophy (2), Lady Byng Memorial Trophy (2), Hart Memorial Trophy (2), Jack Adams Award (2), Ted Lindsay Award (1), and William M. Jennings Trophy (1).

2. Since the following trophies were introduced, nobody from the franchise has ever won the James Norris Memorial Trophy as the NHL's best defenseman; the Frank J. Selke Trophy for the league's best defensive forward; the Vezina Trophy for the top goaltender; and the Bill Masterton Memorial Trophy for the player who best exemplifies the qualities of sportsmanship, perseverance, and dedication.

3. Five players have won the Calder Trophy as the NHL Rookie of the Year. Peter Stastny kicked things off in 1980-81 with Quebec and was followed in 1994-95 by Peter Forsberg, also for Quebec. Since moving to Colorado, Chris Drury was the winner in 1998-99, followed by Gabriel Landeskog for 2011-12, and Nathan MacKinnon for 2013-14.

4. The Conn Smythe Trophy for the MVP of the playoffs has

been won by two Avalanche players. Joe Sakic was honored in 1995-96 when he tallied 18 goals and 34 points in 22 games, including a league-record six game-winning goals. Netminder Patrick Roy followed in 2000-01 by winning the trophy for a record third time with a 1.70 goals-against average and a .934 save percentage in 23 games.

5. A pair of Colorado skaters has been rewarded for their sportsmanship, ability, and gentlemanly conduct with the Lady Byng Trophy. Joe Sakic was named the winner for his play in 2000-01 and was followed by fellow center Ryan O'Reilly in 2013-14.

6. From 1927 to 1981, the Vezina Trophy was awarded to the team allowing the fewest regular-season goals. Since 1982, it has been given to the NHL's top goalie, while the William M. Jennings Award was introduced for the fewest goals conceded by a team. No player has won the Vezina while playing for the franchise, but Patrick Roy won the Jennings Trophy in 2001-02.

7. The Hart Memorial Trophy is awarded to the player deemed most valuable to his team during the regular season. Avs players to take this honor have been centers Joe Sakic in 2000-01 and Peter Forsberg in 2002-03.

8. The Ted Lindsay Award is given to the player who was chosen as the most valuable in the regular season by his peers in the NHL Players' Association (NHLPA). The lone franchise winner in this category was Joe Sakic for his play in 2000-01.

9. The only franchise player to lead the NHL in scoring was center Peter Forsberg for his 106 points in 2002-03. In addition, winger Milan Hejduk captured the Rocket Richard Award that season for leading the league in goals with an even 50 and also added 48 assists.

10. Two franchise coaches have been awarded the Jack Adams Award over the years for being named coach of the year for their work in the regular season. Marc Crawford took the honors in 1994-95 with the Quebec Nordiques, while Patrick Roy won it with Colorado in 2013-14.

# CONCLUSION

The book you've just read is filled with over 40 years' worth of fascinating trivia, facts, and anecdotes concerning the Colorado Avalanche franchise. It dates back to 1979, when the club was based in Canada and known as the Quebec Nordiques.

We hope we've entertained and perhaps educated Avs fans along the way with the information we've offered and brought back some exciting memories from the franchise's history.

The franchise has consistently thrilled and entertained its fans from its beginnings in Quebec and continues to do so in Colorado.

We've taken a fun and lighthearted approach to the book and have included information on numerous players, coaches, and general managers. However, we apologize if we have missed your favorites while compiling the information.

The most loyal and passionate Avalanche supporters may very well know the majority of answers to the quiz chapters and may even be able to teach us a thing or two. But there may also be a few tidbits of information that are new to them. Either way, the trivia book is an ideal way to arm yourself with knowledge when taking on fellow fans in trivia challenges.

The Avalanche became a smash hit when they arrived in Colorado and proved they weren't just one-hit wonders. The team has been one of the most consistent in the NHL since 1995 and is known for icing some of the best young hockey talent the world has to offer.

The franchise's fans have followed the team through thick and thin, and from Quebec to Denver to prove they're among the most loyal on the planet.

Here's to being one of them and thanks for taking the time to read the club's latest trivia book.

Made in United States
Troutdale, OR
12/11/2023

15680286R00086